McGRAW-HILL READING

Consulting Authors

Barbara Coulter, Frankie Dungan, Joseph B. Rubin,
Carl B. Smith, Shirley Wright

Contributors

The Princeton Review, Time Magazine

The Princeton Review is not
affiliated with Princeton
University or ETS.

McGraw-Hill School Division

A Division of The McGraw·Hill Companies

McGraw-Hill School Division
Two Penn Plaza
New York, New York 10121

Printed in the United States of America

ISBN 0-02-184724-X/3, Book 1

2 3 4 5 6 7 8 9 043/027 04 03 02 01 00

Macmillan/McGraw-Hill Edition

McGRAW-HILL READING

Authors

James Flood
Jan E. Hasbrouck
James V. Hoffman
Diane Lapp
Angela Shelf Medearis
Scott Paris
Steven Stahl
Josefina Villamil Tinajero
Karen D. Wood

McGraw-Hill
School Division

New York   Farmington

UNIT 1

Great Adventures

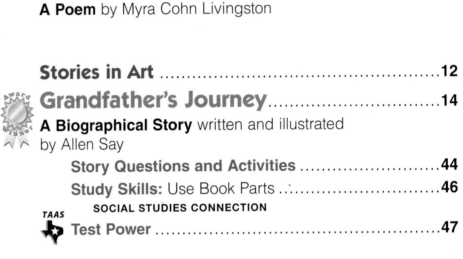

UNIT 2

Nature Links

UNIT 3

Be Creative!

Great Adventures

Closed, I am a Mystery

Closed, I am a mystery.
Open, I will always be
a friend with whom you think and see.

Closed, there's nothing I can say.
Open, we can dream and stray
to other worlds, far and away.

by Myra Cohn Livingston

Some paintings seem to tell a story. There are many details which add to the story. Each tells us something about what is happening.

Look at this setting. What can you tell about it? Did the people live a long time ago? How can you tell? Where do you think the people are going? How do they feel?

Close your eyes. Think about the painting. What do you remember? Why?

The Emigrants by Thomas Falcon

MEET ALLEN SAY

Allen Say has been an artist almost all of his life. At the age of thirteen, he already had a job drawing backgrounds for a famous cartoonist in Japan. When Say came to the United States, his interest in art kept growing. In time he began to write and illustrate his own stories.

Say begins creating a story by drawing the pictures first. Then he thinks of a story idea and the words to go with his drawings. Say tries to produce a book a year, which he admits is hard work. But he says, "I love what I'm doing so much that although it's difficult, it makes me happy."

Other books that you might enjoy by this writer and illustrator are *The Lost Lake*, *El Chino*, and *Tree of Cranes*.

Grandfather's Journey

WRITTEN AND ILLUSTRATED BY
ALLEN SAY

My grandfather was a young man when he left his
home in Japan and went to see the world.

He wore European clothes for the first time and
began his journey on a steamship. The Pacific Ocean
astonished him.

For three weeks he did not see land. When land finally appeared it was the New World.

He explored North America by train and riverboat,
and often walked for days on end.

Deserts with rocks like enormous sculptures amazed
him.

The endless farm fields reminded him of the ocean he
had crossed.

Huge cities of factories and tall buildings bewildered
and yet excited him.

He marveled at the towering mountains and rivers as clear as the sky.

He met many people along the way. He shook hands
with black men and white men, with yellow men and
red men.

The more he traveled, the more he longed to see new places, and never thought of returning home.

Of all the places he visited, he liked California best.
He loved the strong sunlight there, the Sierra
Mountains, the lonely seacoast.

After a time, he returned to his village in Japan to marry his childhood sweetheart. Then he brought his bride to the new country.

They made their home by the San Francisco Bay and had a baby girl.

As his daughter grew, my grandfather began to think about his own childhood. He thought about his old friends.

He remembered the mountains and rivers of his home. He surrounded himself with songbirds, but he could not forget.

Finally, when his daughter was nearly grown, he
could wait no more. He took his family and returned
to his homeland.

Once again he saw the mountains and rivers of his childhood. They were just as he had remembered them.

Once again he exchanged stories and laughed with
his old friends.

But the village was not a place for a daughter from
San Francisco. So my grandfather bought a house in
a large city nearby.

There, the young woman fell in love, married, and
sometime later I was born.

When I was a small boy, my favorite weekend was a
visit to my grandfather's house. He told me many
stories about California.

He raised warblers and silvereyes, but he could not forget the mountains and rivers of California. So he planned a trip.

But a war began. Bombs fell from the sky and
scattered our lives like leaves in a storm.

When the war ended, there was nothing left of the
city and of the house where my grandparents
had lived.

So they returned to the village where they had been children. But my grandfather never kept another songbird.

The last time I saw him, my grandfather said that he longed to see California one more time. He never did.

And when I was nearly grown, I left home and went
to see California for myself.

After a time, I came to love the land my grandfather had loved, and I stayed on and on until I had a daughter of my own.

But I also miss the mountains and rivers of my childhood. I miss my old friends. So I return now and then, when I can not still the longing in my heart.

The funny thing is, the moment I am in one country, I am homesick for the other.

I think I know my grandfather now.
I miss him very much.

Story Questions & Activities

1. What were three things that the grandfather saw when he came to North America?

2. At first, how did the grandfather feel about his travels?

3. What do you think he missed most when he was living in the United States?

4. What is the main idea of this selection?

5. If the grandfather could talk to the people in the picture on pages 12–13, what might he tell them?

Write a Letter

Think about a trip you have taken. Write a letter to your best friend telling about the place you visited and how you got there. Include lots of details about the place.

44

Draw a Picture

Think about the times you have spent with a grandparent or an older adult. Choose one special time that you shared together. Draw a picture that shows your experience.

Save a Memory

Choose a special moment from your life and think of a way to help you remember it. Create a "remembering" device, such as a box of objects, a photo collection, a poem, or a story. Display your "remembering" device in the classroom.

Find Out More

If you could move to a faraway place, where would it be? Find that place on a map and trace a route there. Then find out three things you did not know about this place. Use an encyclopedia or a travel guide.

Use Book Parts

Has life in Japan changed much since the grandfather's time? You can find out by looking at a book about Japan. The **cover** and **table of contents** of one book about Japan are shown below.

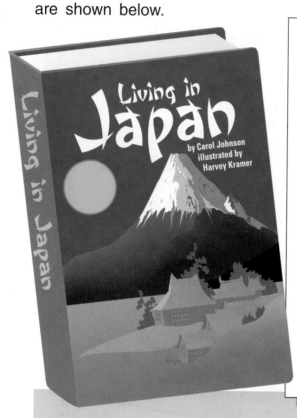

~ LIVING IN JAPAN ~

Use the cover and table of contents to answer these questions.

1 What is the title of the book?

2 Who are the author and the illustrator?

3 How many chapters does the book have?

4 On what pages could you find information about family traditions?

5 If you wanted to learn about holidays in Japan, would this be a good book to check? Why or why not?

DIRECTIONS:

Read the story. Then read each question about the story.

SAMPLE

The Discovery

Tony and Jennie played in a field by Jennie's house one day. They were digging in the dirt to build a fort. Jennie's fingers hit a flat, sharp rock.

"What is this?" Jennie asked. She picked up a rock shaped like a triangle.

"Wow! That's an arrowhead!" Tony said. He looked at the rock. "I read that Native Americans made arrows from straight sticks," he said. "They used stone for the tips of the arrows and tied them to the end of the sticks."

Jennie put the arrowhead into her pocket. "Let's give this arrowhead to the museum. Then everyone can learn more about arrowheads," she said.

1 When Jennie picked up the arrowhead, Tony was—

○ angry

○ sad

○ surprised

○ tired

2 Where was Jennie digging?

○ At the museum

○ In the yard outside the school

○ In a field near Jennie's house

○ In Tony's backyard

Stories in Art

Some paintings are filled with many details. You find yourself looking carefully at the picture to discover what is happening.

Look at this painting. What can you tell about it? How does the artist show you that it is a race? Pretend that you are one of the bicycle riders. What would you do to try to win the race?

Close your eyes. What do you remember about the painting? Why?

Heroes on Wheels
by Jane Wooster Scott

49

Meet Barney Saltzberg

Things are always hopping at Barney Saltzberg's house. In addition to two dogs, a cat, a fish, and a hamster named Pinky, he also keeps a bunch of frogs.

Even with a house full of pets, Saltzberg has still managed to find time to write and illustrate several award-winning and correctly spelled picture books for children. You might also like to read *This Is a Great Place for a Hot Dog Stand*, *Mrs. Morgan's Lawn*, and *Backyard Cowboy*.

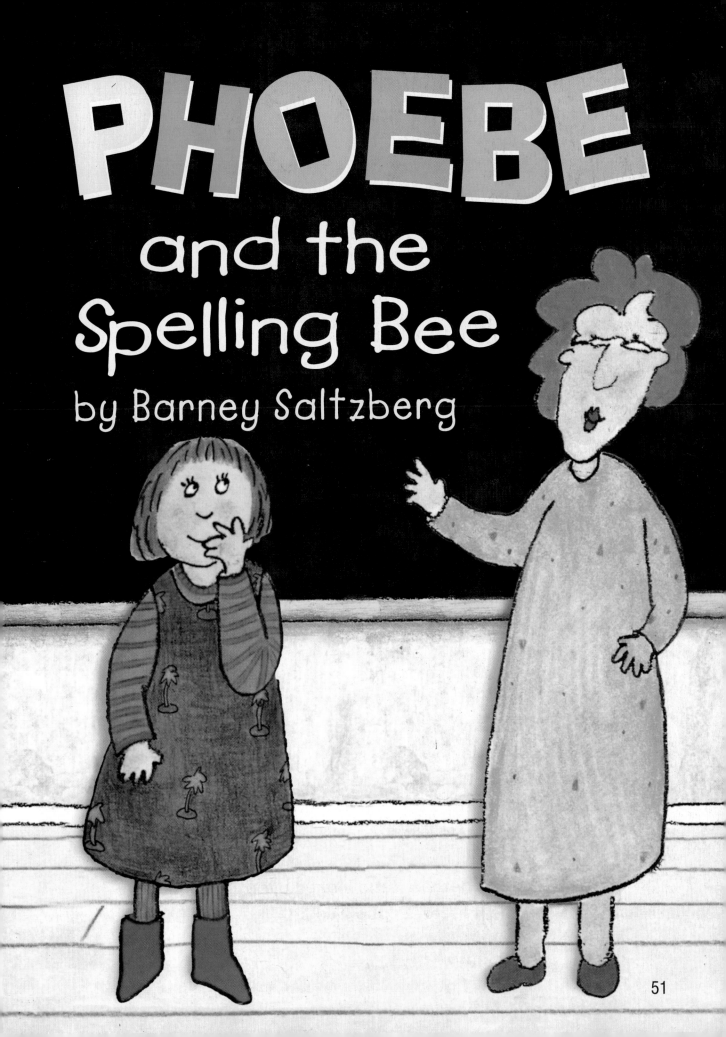

PHOEBE
and the
Spelling Bee
by Barney Saltzberg

"Friday we will have our first spelling bee," announced
Ms. Ravioli. "Here's a list of words you should know."

I slid down in my chair. "I'm going to be sick on Friday,"
I whispered to Katie.

"Don't be silly, Phoebe," said Katie. "Spelling is easy."

"I'm allergic to spelling," I told her.

"I'll help you," said Katie.

We ate lunch together. Katie looked over the spelling
list. "This will be a breeze!" she said.

I drew dots all over my arm and started groaning, "Oooohhhh!"

"What's the matter?" asked Katie.

"I think I've got chicken pox!" I said.

"Spell **actor**," said Katie.

"**A-k-d-o-r**," I said.

"That's what it sounds like," said Katie, "but it's spelled differently."

She showed me the word on the spelling list. I saw that you could break the word into two parts—**act** and **or**.

"If I could **act or** spell, I'd **act!**" I said. "**A-c-t-o-r!**"

"That's right!" said Katie.

"Try spelling **brontosaurus**," said Katie.

I dropped to the ground, holding my leg. "Oh, it's broken!" I cried. "A **brontosaurus** knocked me over, and I broke my leg!"

"I'm waiting!" said Katie.
"Race you to class backward," I shouted, and then I ran inside.

That night Katie called me to find out how I was doing with my spelling list.

"Great!" I said.

I was folding the spelling list into a paper airplane.

The next morning Ms. Ravioli asked how many
students had been studying for the spelling bee.

Everyone raised their hand. Except me. I was under
the table, studying my shoes.

"Phoebe," said Ms. Ravioli, "have you looked at your
spelling list?"

I sat up in my chair. "Once there was an **actor** who
played a **brontosaurus**."

Everybody laughed. I sank in my chair.

"Settle down, class," said Ms. Ravioli. "It sounds like Phoebe has an unusual way of learning her words."

I looked at Katie's spelling list on our way home.

"Try spelling **graceful**," she said.

"The **actor** who played a **brontosaurus** was **graceful**!" I said.

"You're great at making up stories," said Katie.
"But the spelling bee is in three days!"

"I know," I said. Then I ran to get some ice cream.

I knew I had better study or I would really embarrass
myself at the spelling bee.

I found my spelling list on my bedroom floor, still folded into an airplane.

"If I can fly this into the trash can on the first try," I thought, "I'll be the winner of the spelling bee."

The plane flew under a chair.
"That was just a warm-up."

The plane flew into the wall.
"Didn't count."

I stood on a chair
and dropped the airplane
into the trash.
"Yes!"

I had a victory celebration
and danced around my room.
Then my father told me
it was time to go to bed.

The next morning Ms. Ravioli said we would have a mock spelling bee.

I decided it was time to get sick.

"Ooooh!" I moaned.

"What seems to be the problem?" asked Ms. Ravioli.

"I ate too many pieces of pizza with pineapple last night," I said. "I feel sick."

"I think a visit to the nurse's office would be a good idea," said Ms. Ravioli.

"You haven't studied at all, have you?" whispered Katie.

"Yes I have!" I said.

I dragged my feet to the nurse's office. Now my stomach really did feel awful.

I had never lied to Katie before.

When I got back from the nurse's office, Katie handed me a note. It said:

YOU DIDN'T STUDY AND YOU DIDN'T HAVE A STOMACHACHE AND REAL FRIENDS TELL EACH OTHER THE TRUTH!

I didn't speak to Katie for the rest of the day.

That night I felt terrible. I hadn't been honest with my best friend, and I wasn't ready for the spelling bee.

I looked at my spelling list.

The first word I learned was **method**. I thought of a caveman saying his name, "**Me**, **Thod**."

I learned **telephone** by thinking of a phone, which you *tell* your friends things on. The second **l** in **tell** becomes an **e**.

I even learned how to spell **consonant**. It was easy because I figured there were three parts, **con**, **son**, and **ant**.

The next day was Friday. Spelling bee day.

I brought Katie a tulip and said I was sorry for having lied.

Ms. Ravioli explained the rules. I could feel my heart beating fast. What if I looked stupid in front of the whole class?

I started to raise my hand to go to the nurse's office. I decided to have the flu.

Katie wished me good luck. I was happy she was still talking to me. I put down my hand.

I decided not to have the flu after all.

During the spelling bee, Sheldon couldn't spell **disaster**. So he had to sit down.

When Jorge couldn't spell **telephone** correctly, he asked to go to the bathroom.

Marcia almost remembered how to spell **consonant**, but she forgot one of the **n**s.

I had to spell **Wednesday**. I knew the word had three parts, all with three letters.

I thought of a wedding day where chocolate chips were thrown instead of rice. **Wed** for wedding, **nes** for Nestlé chocolate, and **day**!

I spelled the word, "**W-e-d-n-e-s-d-a-y**."

"Nice job!" said Ms. Ravioli.

Katie spelled her word perfectly.
"**N-a-t-u-r-a-l**," she said.

After a while there were only three of us
still spelling, and then came **brontosaurus**. I
tried sounding it out,
"**b-r-a-w-n-t-o-e-s-o-r-u-s**."

"That was a good try," said Ms. Ravioli,
"but it's not the correct spelling."

"The **actor** was a **natural** and very **graceful**," I said.
The whole class was staring at me.

"The **a-c-t-o-r** played a **brontosaurus** and met a caveman who said, '**Me, Thod**,' which is how you break down the spelling of **method**. Thod asked the dinosaur if he had heard about the volcano **disaster**. The dinosaur said no, but he wondered if Thod knew what a **c-o-n-s-o-n-a-n-t** was."

I looked at Ms. Ravioli.

"Please continue," she said.

So I did. "Thod and the dinosaur heard a **t-e-l-e-p-h-o-n-e** ringing in a tree!"

Katie smiled.

"The call was for a **p-e-d-e-s-t-r-i-a-n** who was jogging by, eating a piece of **c-h-o-c-o-l-a-t-e**." I told my class that a great way to remember how to spell chocolate is to think of someone named *Choco*, who's *late*.

"When Choco saw the **brontosaurus**, he screamed and ran the other way! The caveman and the dinosaur fell on the ground and laughed!"

"That's the **l-e-g-e-n-d** of Thod and the brontosaurus. You can remember how to spell **legend** by thinking of your **leg** and **end**!"

Everybody clapped when I finished. Even though I couldn't spell **brontosaurus**, I had used up all the words on my list to tell a story. Charlie couldn't spell **brontosaurus** either—but Katie could, so she won the spelling bee. She was great!

Ms. Ravioli gave Katie a certificate that said CHAMPION SPELLER.

I got a certificate, too, only mine said WONDERFUL IMAGINATION!

Story Questions & Activities

1. Why did Phoebe pretend to feel sick?

2. What was unusual about the way that Phoebe learned to spell words?

3. Did you think that Phoebe might win the spelling bee? Explain.

4. What is this story mostly about?

5. Phoebe got ready for the spelling bee by thinking of a clever way to learn the words. How do you think the bike racers in the painting on pages 48–49 got ready for their race?

Write a Personal Narrative

Have you ever been in an exciting contest, such as a race or a game? Write about what happened. Tell how you felt before, during, and after the contest.

74

Create a Poster

Gather information about the brontosaurus or another dinosaur. Use what you learn to make a poster. Include a drawing and some fun facts.

Make Your Own Spelling Book

Choose three words that you find difficult to spell. Write each word on one side of a piece of paper. On the other side, draw a picture that will remind you of how to spell the word. Punch a hole in the pages and tie them together with yarn to make a book.

Find Out More

Many words, like *consonant*, can be broken into smaller words. Flip through a dictionary and find a few such words. Then, with a partner, play a game of charades and try to guess each other's words.

Use a Glossary

A **glossary** can help you to spell a word correctly or to learn the meaning of a word. The words in a glossary appear in alphabetical order. Guide words at the top tell you the first and last words on the page.

B

bamboo A tall plant that is related to grass. The bamboo has woody stems that are often hollow and are used to make fishing poles, canes, and furniture. *Noun.*
—Made of *bamboo. Adjective.*
bam•boo (bam bü′) *noun, plural* **bamboos;** *adjective.*

Word History
The word **bamboo** comes from the Malay word *bambu* for the same plant.

bamboo

Bapa Raja (bä′pə rä′jə).

beneath 1. Lower than; below; under. We stood *beneath* the stars. 2. Unworthy of. Telling a lie is *beneath* you.
be•neath (bi nēth′) *preposition.*

bound 1. To leap; spring; jump. The rabbit *bounded* away into the woods. 2. To spring back after hitting something. The ball *bounded* off the wall and hit my bicycle.
bound (bound) *verb,* **bounded, bounding.**

brontosaurus A huge, plant-eating dinosaur with a long neck and tail and a small head. This dinosaur is also called *brontosaur.*
bron•to•saurus (bron′tə sôrəs′) *noun.*

buffalo A large North American animal that has a big hump on its back; bison. Many years ago *buffalo* roamed free on the plains.
buf•fa•lo (buf′ ə lō) *noun, plural* **buffaloes** or **buffalos** or **buffalo.**

Use the glossary to answer these questions.

1 What word comes before *brontosaurus* in the **glossary**?

2 Is *brontosaurus* a noun, a verb, or an adjective?

3 To find out what the word *actor* means, would you look before or after this page in the glossary? Explain.

4 What are the guide words for the page on which *brontosaurus* appears?

5 Which do you think a brontosaurus would rather eat, meat or leaves?

TAAS

Test Tip
Read each question carefully before you answer it.

DIRECTIONS:
Read the story. Then read each question about the story.

SAMPLE

A Pet for Bobby

Bobby's new dog Lucky did not listen. Every time Bobby said, "Sit," Lucky wagged his tail. Bobby was worried.

One day, Bobby had an idea. He went to the kitchen and got some dog biscuits. Then he went out to the backyard. Lucky came up to him, his tail wagging.

"Sit, Lucky! Sit!" Bobby said. But Lucky just wagged his tail.

Bobby took out a dog biscuit and held it above Lucky's head. Lucky just looked at the biscuit.

"Sit, Lucky!" Bobby said. Lucky did not understand. Bobby moved the biscuit a little until Lucky had to sit back to keep it in sight. "Sit, Lucky!"

Bobby said as Lucky sat. Bobby petted his dog and gave him the biscuit as a reward.

1 The next time he wants Lucky to listen, Bobby will probably—

○ not be able to find Lucky

○ get a dog biscuit for Lucky

○ get Lucky's leash

○ bring a friend's dog over

2 How did Bobby feel when he first tried to get Lucky to sit?

○ Happy

○ Sad

○ Quiet

○ Worried

77

Stories in Art

Look at the painting quickly. What did you see? Look at it again. What is happening to the leaves? What other details can you see?

Sometimes a painting seems to change before your eyes. You may need to look at it carefully to see everything that is going on.

Close your eyes. What do you remember about the painting? Why?

The Art of Conversation
by René Magritte

78

MEET

ARLINE AND JOSEPH BAUM

Arline and Joseph Baum are a husband-and-wife team who are fascinated by the art of illusion. Arline Baum once worked as an assistant to a magician. Joseph Baum was an art director for an advertising agency. His ability to create illusions with art won him many awards.

In *Opt: An Illusionary Tale,* the Baums have created a land of optical illusions. The book begins like this: "Seeing is believing, but sometimes our eyes deceive us. When this happens, it is called an optical illusion. Opt is a land of optical illusions." This book won an award for being an outstanding science trade book.

AN ILLUSIONARY TALE

OPT

BY ARLINE AND JOSEPH BAUM

A Sunny Day in Opt, a day of banners, balloons, and surprises

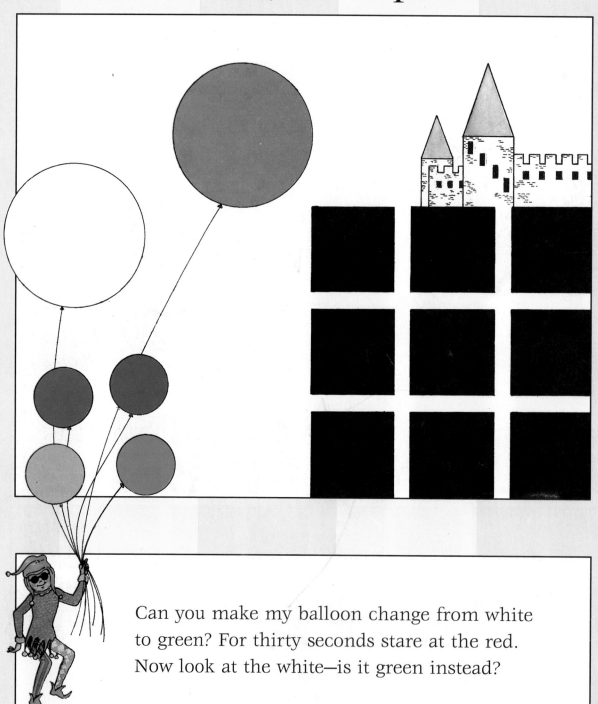

Can you make my balloon change from white to green? For thirty seconds stare at the red. Now look at the white—is it green instead?

The Wall surrounding the castle

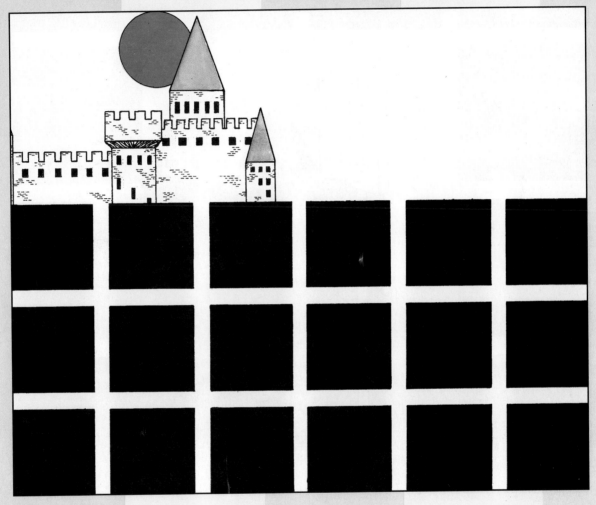

Where white lines cross, gray dots are seen.
One disappears where one has been.

The Castle Guard with his trident

How many prongs do you see?
I see two on the bottom—but on the top, three.

The Royal Messenger arriving with a letter for the King

The vertical lines of the messenger's cloak are crooked.
The red tape on the letter is longer than the blue.
But is this really true?
Remember, now you are in OPT!

The Trumpeters announcing the arrival of the messenger

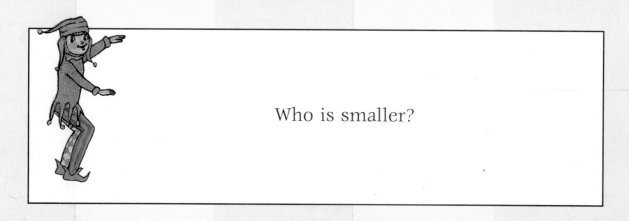

Who is smaller?

The King and Queen waiting for the message

Who is taller?

The Message for the King to read

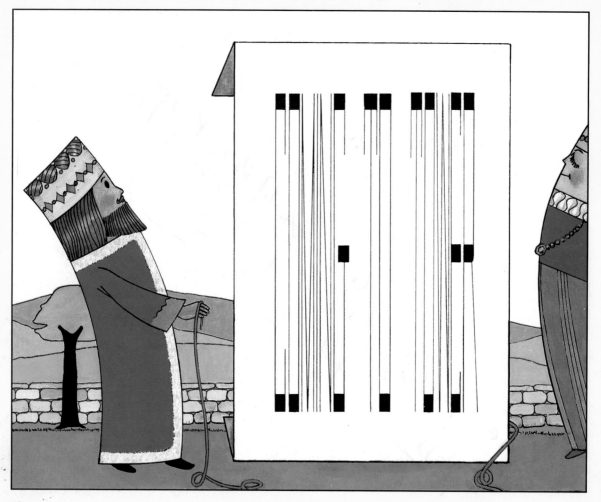

A clue to make the message clear.
First tilt the book, then take a look.
Who sent the message?

The Royal Art Gallery, dusted and tidied

Are the top of the lampshade and the top of the lamp base the same length?
Two ladies framed—or is it four?
Hidden elsewhere, you'll see two more.

The Prince goes fishing with his new rod

Which is the rod and which the branch of the tree?
Now look at the Prince's shirt.
What do you see?
Is the space between the shirt's black dots
larger than those same black spots?

The Princess picking a special bouquet

Flowers fair, flowers bright.
Which flower center is larger—
the black or the white?

The Great Hall, ready for the party

Should the Queen straighten the mirror on the wall?
There are eight more faces.
Can you find them all?

The Opt Sign pointing the way to the zoo

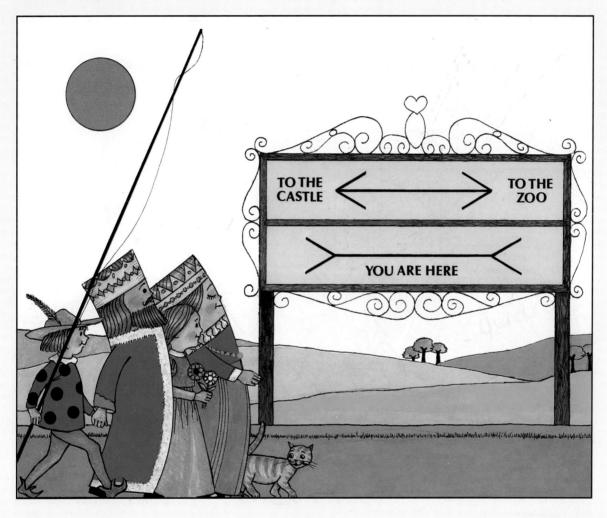

By the sign the royal family will stop.
Which line is longer, the bottom or top?
The King knows who the guest will be.
So do I—just follow me.

The Opt Zoo, home of amazing animals

Faces within faces can be found—
if you just turn the book around.
Is the body of the royal pet shorter than its neck?
Is the height of the zookeeper's hat the same as

The Zookeeper and the Royal Pet hearing the news

the width of its brim?
For thirty seconds stare at the star that is blue.
Now look at white paper—a colorful change,
just for you.

The Pavilion decorated with banners

Are the banners light green or dark green,
light pink or dark pink?
Some say they're the same shade.
But what do *you* think?

The Tower with guard spotting the guest

The guard marches up, stair by stair—
but is he getting anywhere?
He sees the guest.
Who can it be?
Turn the page and you will see!

The Guest is here!

The fire-snorting dragon now comes in.
Turn the book and his eyes will spin.
Arriving with presents—and none too late.
But did he tie the red ribbons on straight?

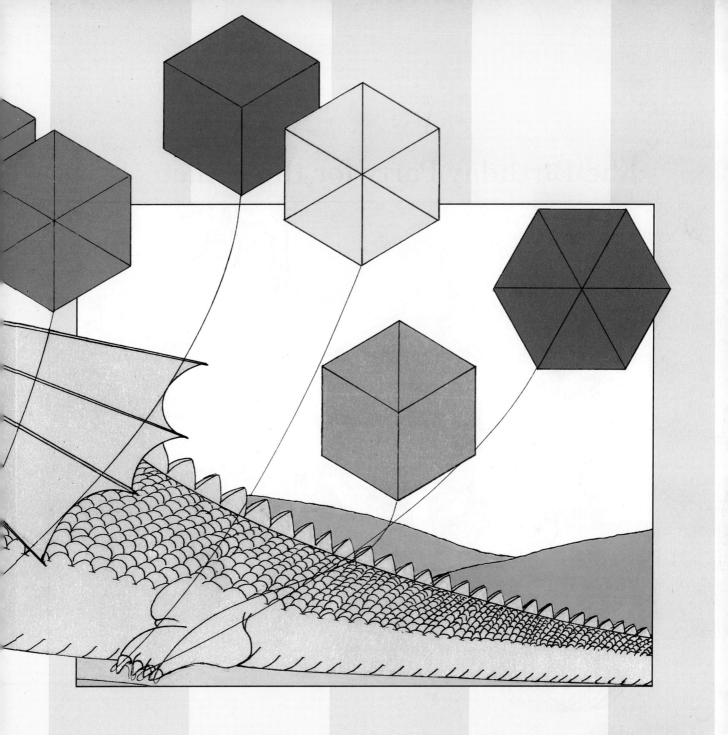

Look closely at the bright kites in the air.
Do flat kites or box kites float up there?

The Birthday Party for the Prince

This gift, unwrapped, tells the Prince's age.
This is what the dragon said,
"Six blocks become seven if you stand on your head.
HAPPY BIRTHDAY!"

The Dragon saying good-bye

The dragon was a perfect guest.
The party was a great success.
But *you* don't have to go away,
come join me in Opt any day.

Story Questions & Activities

1 Where does this story take place?

2 What is your favorite illusion in Opt? Explain how it works.

3 What is the most important rule to follow in the land of Opt?

4 What is this story mainly about?

5 What if Phoebe found herself in the land of Opt? What would she do?

Write a Story

Write a story about a time when something turned out to be different from what you expected. Maybe a scary sound was actually the wind. Be sure your story has a beginning, middle, and end.

Create an Optical Illusion

Follow these steps to make your own optical illusion.

1. Use a ruler to draw two parallel lines four inches long. Draw the lines about one inch apart.
2. On the top line, draw a V pointing inward at each end of the line.
3. On the bottom line, draw a V pointing outward at each end.
4. Ask a friend if one of the lines looks longer.

Make a Travel Brochure

Make a travel brochure for the land of Opt. Tell why people should visit there and describe some of the strange things they will see. Draw pictures to go along with your descriptions.

Find Out More

What would you like to know about real-life castles? Find out more. Share what you learn by creating castle fact cards and displaying them in your classroom.

Use a Table of Contents

"Opt: An Illusionary Tale" blends science fact with fantasy in an unusual way. With most other books, it is easier to tell whether they are **fiction** or **nonfiction.** A book that tells about made-up characters and events is **fiction.** A book that tells about real people, places, and things is **nonfiction.**

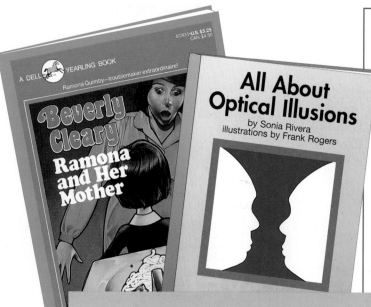

Contents

Use the book covers and table of contents to answer these questions.

1 Which of these two books is nonfiction?

2 In which book would you find information about illusions?

3 If you finished chapter three of *Ramona and Her Mother* last night, what page should you turn to today?

4 Does the chapter "The Telephone Call" tell about a real or a made-up event? Explain.

5 What do you think a chapter title in *All About Optical Illusions* might be?

DIRECTIONS:
Read the story. Then read each question about the story.

SAMPLE

The Essay Contest

Arabella sat at the table and looked at a contest flyer.

Rules:
Write about a real person.
The essay should be three pages long and your name should be on each page.

Schedule:
May 1 Essays turned in to teacher
May 2 Essays judged
May 8 Winners announced

Prizes:
All prizes will be given the last day of school.
First-prize essays will be entered in the State Fair.
Second-prize essays will receive a book.

1 To follow the rules, Arabella should—

○ write about an imaginary person

○ write her name on every page of her essay

○ write an essay that is five pages long

○ write about a wild animal

2 To enter the contest, Arabella must turn in her essay by—

○ May 1

○ May 2

○ May 5

○ May 8

Why are your answers correct?

Stories in Art

An artist can tell a story. Sometimes you can almost hear what the people in the picture are saying.

Look at the picture. What do you think it is about? What do you think the boy holding the pitcher of lemonade is saying? How do you think the children could get more customers to buy their lemonade?

The artist made this picture many years ago. If the artist were to make it today, how might it look different?

Lemonade Stand
by Norman Rockwell
The Norman Rockwell Museum,
Stockbridge, Massachusetts

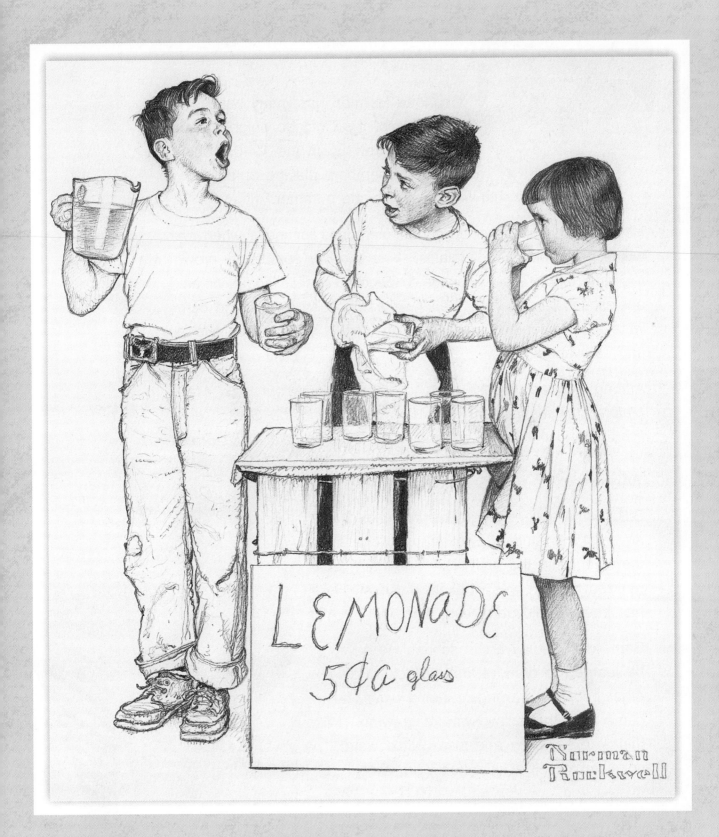

Meet

CHARLOTTE HERMAN

Charlotte Herman has many happy memories of the Chicago neighborhood where she grew up in the 1940s. She especially remembers playing outdoors with her friends during the summer.

Herman often uses her childhood memories for ideas when she writes her books. She explains, "I have never completely grown up, it seems, and it's easy for me to become a child again, or an adolescent. I hope I'm a better writer because of this and can write about people that readers can identify with and believe in and care about."

Among Herman's books are two other books about Max, *Max Malone, the Magnificent* and *Max Malone and the Great Cereal Rip-Off,* and the award-winning *The House on Walenska Street.*

Meet B.B. SAMS

B.B. Sams never thought he would become an artist. He studied English in college and then went into the navy. But eventually, he realized that art was what he did best. He has been an illustrator ever since.

Sams didn't study art in school. He says he learned to draw at first by looking at other people's drawings. After a while, he came up with his own way of drawing. "I like things to be funny and also a little weird," he says. "I still consider myself a kid when I draw, so I put in things that interest me."

MAX MALONE

By Charlotte Herman

Illustrated by
B.B. Sams

Baseballs for Sale

"Austin Healy is having his appendix out today," said Max.

"Yeah, I heard about that," said Gordy. "He threw up all his popcorn last night. Too bad he has to miss Dusty Field on Friday."

Max and Gordy were on their way to Toys for Less. They each had two dollars and fifty cents to spend at the store's Giant Summer Clearance Sale.

When they reached the store, they saw signs on all the windows:

"I hope we find some good stuff," said Max as they went inside. They walked past the first few counters, which displayed the inexpensive toys and prizes like the ones they'd bought for their carnival. They were looking for more expensive, quality items. Max hoped to find something worth five dollars for half off. Then he would have enough money. He didn't have to look far. The idea hit him the moment he saw them.

"That's it!" he cried out. "That's perfect."

"What's it? What's perfect?" asked Gordy.

Max pointed to a box of rubber baseballs. A sign on the box read: 20 CENTS EACH.

"Don't you see? We buy these baseballs for twenty cents each. Then we sell them at a higher price to people who want Dusty Field's autograph."

"You're a genius," said Gordy, slapping Max on the back. "That's a great idea. All we have to do is figure out how many balls we can buy for our five dollars." He looked up at the ceiling and concentrated. "Let's see now. If each ball costs twenty cents, and we have five dollars . . . I forget . . . Do we divide or multiply?"

"We divide," said Max, writing and erasing in the air. "Twenty cents into five dollars . . . "

Gordy was impressed. "How many can we buy, Max?"

"Hold your horses. I have to move the decimals."

Max continued writing, but he stopped suddenly in midair. "Wait. I have another idea. First we have to see the manager."

Max's eyes searched the store for someone who looked like a manager. He saw a young woman walking around, giving orders to the workers.

"That must be the manager," he said, walking toward her.

Gordy followed, and a few minutes later Max was asking, "Excuse me, but are you the manager?"

"Yes," said the young woman. "Can I help you?"

"I was wondering," said Max. "If we buy those rubber baseballs in quantity, how much will you sell them for?"

The manager looked up at the ceiling the way Gordy had done. Max waited nervously.

"How much do you want to spend?" she asked after a while.

"Five dollars—including tax," he answered.

"I'll tell you what. Summer's over. And I need the space more than I need the baseballs. For five dollars—including tax—you can have the whole box. There should be close to fifty balls in there."

"Fifty?" Max cried out. "It's a deal."

"Forty-eight baseballs at fifty cents apiece. We'll really make a fortune, almost," said Max.

"Forty-six," Gordy corrected. "We have to save two for ourselves."

It was Friday morning, and Max and Gordy, each carrying a bag of baseballs, were on their way to the sporting-goods store. It was only nine thirty, and the store didn't open until ten. But they wanted to get there early so they wouldn't miss a single person.

A long line of kids was already forming in front of the store. "Everyone wants to meet Dusty Field," said Max.

"My father said his autograph might become valuable some day," said Gordy. "A real collectible."

Some of the kids had come prepared with baseballs or mitts for autographing. Some had autograph books, and a few were holding scraps of paper. But most of them didn't have anything. Max was sure that lots of people would want the baseballs. Well, he was almost sure. He knew he should start selling right away, but he couldn't make himself move. His legs felt like spaghetti. Thinking about selling had been a lot easier than actually doing it. There were so many people. What if nobody wanted to buy any baseballs? What if he and Gordy got chased away by the store owner? Or the police?

Rosalie had warned him about that. She said that he and Gordy needed a license to sell the baseballs. Max didn't know if she knew what she was talking about. He had heard of a dog license. And a license to drive a car. But never a license to sell baseballs.

"What are we waiting for?" asked Gordy.

"You go first," said Max.

"No, you first. It was your idea."

"We'll go together," said Max. He dipped his hand into the bag and pulled out two baseballs. He forced himself to walk along the line of kids and call out, "Baseballs for sale. Just fifty cents." He waved the balls around so everyone could see them. A few people glanced in Max's direction, but turned away.

Gordy, in the meantime, was calling out, "Get your baseballs autographed by Dusty Field. Just fifty cents. Sure to become a collectible."

To his surprise, Max saw that a few kids actually went over to buy some balls from Gordy.

Max then took up the call.

"Get your baseballs autographed by Dusty. Just fifty cents. Sure to become valuable." He didn't want to copy Gordy exactly.

A girl with an autograph book came over to buy a ball. "A baseball is better than an autograph book," she said, handing him the money.

A mother with a small boy came by. "I didn't even think to bring anything that Dusty could sign. This is such a good idea."

Some kids with scraps of paper stuffed the papers into their pockets, or dumped them into trash cans. Then they bought baseballs from Max.

Max was having a great time. He could see that Gordy was too. The scene was just as he had pictured. He was selling what people wanted to buy. And the more he sold, the more confident he became. He even began singing "Take Me Out to the Ball Game." The crowd in front of the store joined in.

Suddenly Max stopped singing. Someone inside the store, the manager probably, was standing at the door, staring at Max. Max stared back, and then looked away. This was it! He and Gordy would be asked to leave. He should have known it was too good to last.

The manager opened the door, and the kids pushed their way in. But the manager disappeared. He was nowhere in sight. Neither were the police.

Max decided that if someone came and told him to stop, he would. But until then, he would keep on selling.

117

He stopped customers before they went into the store. "Get your baseball for Dusty Field's autograph. Fifty cents." Or, "How about a baseball for Dusty's autograph?" Most people were eager to buy.

Dusty was going to be signing autographs until noon. But by eleven, Max and Gordy had sold all their baseballs. All except the two they had saved for themselves.

"I can't believe it," said Max when he and Gordy were waiting in line to meet Dusty. "We sold them all. I thought our goose was cooked when I saw the manager staring at me." Max's mother always used that expression—"my goose was cooked"—even though she had never cooked a goose in her life.

"I can't believe we're getting Dusty's autograph," said Gordy. "I wish the line would move faster. Dusty's hand will get all worn out from shaking hands before he even gets to us."

At last it was Max and Gordy's turn to meet Dusty. Dusty was tall and thin and had a friendly smile. He wasn't wearing a uniform. Just jeans and a T-shirt. But he looked like a ball player anyway.

Max and Dusty shook hands. Dusty said, "Nice to meet you."

But Max couldn't think of anything to say except, "Would you sign this ball to Max?"

"Sure thing," said Dusty, and he signed the ball,
To my pal Max. Dusty Field.

"Wow! Thanks, Dusty."

Gordy couldn't think of anything great to say either. So he handed Dusty his baseball and said, "I'm Gordy."

Dusty signed, *To my pal Gordy. Dusty Field.*

"Wow!" said Gordy.

"This was a great day," said Max.

"Let's go home and split up the money," said Gordy.

"We made a ton," said Max. "And all because we knew the market. We went where the people were. And we bought in quantity. Just like Austin . . . "

Austin. Max had forgotten all about him. Little Austin Healy, who was home with a scar where his appendix should have been. Austin, who was looking forward to meeting Dusty Field. Why, if it weren't for Austin, Max would never have known about Dusty. He and Gordy would never have bought the balls. They never would've made all that money.

"We can't go home yet," said Max. "There's something we have to do first." He led the way to the baseball section of the store. And there, in a bin, were baseballs. Real league baseballs. They cost three dollars, but Max didn't care. He picked one up and showed it to Gordy.

"For Austin," he said.

"We'll get it autographed by Dusty," said Gordy.

They bought the ball and waited in line again.

"Let's see," said Gordy, looking up at the ceiling. "Not counting what we spent on Austin, if we sold forty-six balls at fifty cents each . . . "

"This time we multiply," said Max.

Max Makes a Million

"How nice of you to come," said Austin Healy's mother. "Austin will be so happy to see you. He's been feeling a little low today. He had to miss Dusty Field."

"Maybe we can cheer him up," said Max. He thought of the baseball he had for Austin in his bag, and smiled as he went inside.

They found Austin in his room, feeding Newton some freeze-dried shrimp. Austin was wearing sweatpants and a Mickey Mouse sweatshirt.

"Hey, guys. I was thinking about you all day. Did you get to see Dusty?"

"We just came from there," said Max. "How are you feeling?"

"Okay. Do you want to see my scar?"

Max and Gordy shook their heads. "No thanks," said Max.

Austin fed Newton the last of the shrimp and climbed into bed. "I'm supposed to rest up for a few days. And I'm not supposed to laugh. So don't say anything funny. Just tell me about Dusty."

"The place was mobbed," said Max. "Everyone wanted to see him."

"I wanted to see him," said Austin.

"Yeah, that was too bad. Anyway, we got to shake his hand."

"Wow!" said Austin. "I wanted to shake his hand."

"That's rough," said Max.

"And we got his autograph too," Gordy added.

"Wow! That's what I really wanted most. His autograph."

"Really rough," said Max, shaking his head.

"I might never get another chance to meet Dusty," said Austin, looking glum.

"You might not," said Max.

"I might have to wait forever to get his autograph." Now Austin was looking even more glum.

"I don't think you'll have to wait that long," Max told him. He turned to Gordy and winked. Then he reached into the bag and took out Austin's baseball.

"From Dusty," he said, handing him the ball.

"For me?" asked Austin, turning the ball around so he could read the autograph. "'To my pal Austin. Dusty Field.' Oh, boy! This is great. This is the greatest." Austin was so excited, he practically jumped out of bed.

"Watch out for your stitches," said Max.

Austin turned to Max and Gordy and flashed them a smile. The widest smile they had ever seen on Austin's face. "Thanks, guys. Thanks a million."

"A million? Did you hear that, Gordy?" asked Max, slapping him on the back. "We made our million after all."

Story Questions & Activities

1. What did Max and Gordy do with the baseballs that they bought?

2. Why did the store manager sell them all 48 baseballs for only five dollars?

3. Where else do you think the boys could have sold the baseballs?

4. What is this story mostly about?

5. Max was a good friend to Austin Healy. Think of another story about friendship that you know. How is the main character like Max?

Write an Article

Have you ever done something nice for a friend or relative? Or has someone ever done something really special for you? Write an article about what happened. Include details about how it made you feel.

Create a Bar Graph

Imagine that you have started your own lemonade stand. If you sell 10 cups on the first day, and 20 cups on the second day, how many cups would you need to sell on the third day to have sold 50 cups total? Create a bar graph to show your results.

Perform a Science Trick

You can change your dirty pennies into clean pennies. Put about an inch of vinegar in a cup. Stir in a teaspoon of salt. Put the dirty pennies in the cup. Leave them overnight. In the morning your pennies will look like new.

Find Out More

An autograph can make a baseball card much more valuable. Find out how much the average baseball card costs brand-new. Then find out how much a rare, autographed card might be worth. What cards are worth the most?

STUDY SKILLS

Use an Index

You can learn about the different types of money used throughout the world by checking a nonfiction book such as *Money*. Part of the **index** from that book is below.

Index

A

Africa, 8, 9, 21, 35, 38, 42, 47, 54, 55, 63
altins, 40
America, 24, 38, 39, 57, 62
aqche, 40
assignats, 31, 37
aureus, 36
Australia, 21, 50, 51, 63
Austria, 32, 34, 62

B

bamboo, 52
banknote printing, 16, 17
banknotes, 6, 12, 13, 18, 19, 21, 25, 33, 41,

Botswana, 17, 63
Brazil, 38, 62
Britain, 24, 25, 28, 41, 46, 55
British Columbia, 49
Burma, 7, 63

C

cacao beans, 8
Canada, 21, 48, 49, 62
centimes, 30, 31, 55, 58, 62
cents, 28, 48, 49, 54, 62, 63
Ceylon, 35
Channel Islands, 46, 62
checks, 58, 59
China, 7, 8, 9, 10, 12, 21, 38, 42, 52, 53, 58, 63
Chinese coins, 7, 11, 12,

D

daalder, 35
dalers, 13, 18, 20, 44, 45
decimalization, 4
denarii, 36
Denmark, 42, 43
dollars, 18, 21, 2 29, 48, 49, 50, 57, 58, 62, 63
doubloons, 24,
drachmas, 40,
ducats, 32, 34
dumps, 50

E

ECU, 30
Egypt, 7, 20 55, 63
electrum, 1
England, 1

EYEWITNESS BOOKS

MONEY

Discover the story of money in close-up – its history, its meaning, and its many forms around the world

Use the index to answer these questions.

1 On what pages would you find information about Chinese coins?

2 On what pages should you look for facts about cents?

3 In what type of order do the page numbers in an index entry appear?

4 In what order do the key words in an index appear?

5 Compare this index with the Table of Contents shown on page 104. How are the two types of pages alike? How are they different?

Test Tip

As you read the story, check your understanding of what the story is about.

DIRECTIONS:

Read the story. Then read each question about the story.

SAMPLE

A Surprise for Benny

Cam wanted to help plan her cousin Benny's surprise birthday party. She started to make a list of games to play at the party.

"How about a piñata?" Cam's mom asked.

"What is a piñata?" Cam asked.

"A piñata is a container made of heavy paper that is usually shaped to look like an animal. It is stuffed with candy and prizes and hung from a tree. Everyone is blindfolded and hits the piñata with a stick. When the piñata breaks open, the candy and prizes fall out. Piñatas are always a lot of fun," Cam's mom said.

"What a great idea!" Cam said. "Benny will love that!"

1 How did Cam feel when her mother told her about the piñata?

○ Excited

○ Angry

○ Sad

○ Worried

2 What will Cam probably do next?

○ Make a piñata for the party

○ Cancel the party

○ Decide not to play games

○ Clean up after the party

Stories in Art

This painting almost makes you feel like you can step into the picture. You are closer to the players than the people who are watching them.

Look at this painting. What do you think is happening? What do you think the blue team will try to do? Look at the sky. Do you think it will rain? Why or why not?

Look at the painting again. What other details do you notice about it?

Hockey at Malvern Girls College
by Henry Deykin

TIME

FOR KIDS

SPECIAL REPORT

CHAMPIONS
of the World

On the Ball
A Winning Little League Team

The score is tied 8-8. Chris Cardone steps up to the plate. The pitcher throws the ball. Cardone swings. *Crack!* The ball goes flying. Going, going, gone. The fans go wild. Home run! Cardone rounds the bases. His Little League team from Toms River, New Jersey, pulls ahead. Next time up at bat, Cardone hits another home run!

"When the ball hit the bat, I knew it was gone," says Chris. And get this: It was Cardone's first time up at bat. He was taking the place of another player.

The Toms River team was playing against a team from Japan. Nicknamed the "Beast from the East," Cardone's team won the 1998 Little League World Series. It was the first time since 1993 that a U.S. team had won the series.

"You're out!" A player for the team from Japan gets tagged by Toms River's Brad Frank.

COVER: MIKE SEGAR/ARCHIVE PHOTOS, THIS PAGE: MIKE SEGAR/ARCHIVE PHOTOS

"Way to go!" Todd Frazier's team wins the Little League championship, 12 to 9.

131

The team proudly carries the Little League Championship banner.

"I thought we had it in us," says Todd Frazier. Todd was the star pitcher in the game. He also hit a home run. After the final game, Frazier said he was holding on to a souvenir. "I got my home-run ball right here," he said. "It just means everything to me."

PARADE TIME

After the game, the boys headed back to Toms River. Then it was time for a parade. About 2,000 people came out to cheer them. A plane circled overhead carrying a sign that said, "Welcome Home Toms River East Champs." Signs on homes and cars also celebrated the big win.

The team rode on top of a fire truck and waved to their fans. The kids knew their team was Number One!

Boys and girls both play Little League baseball.

Sammy Sosa

Home-Run Record Race

The 1998 baseball season was a hot one for more than the Toms River Little League team. In pro baseball, a record-breaking home-run race took place between Sammy Sosa and Mark McGwire.

By season's end, Sosa had hit 66 home runs, and McGwire had hit 70. That is the most home runs ever hit by a player in one season. Both men broke the record held by Roger Maris. He hit 61 home runs in 1961.

Mark McGwire

White wool yarn

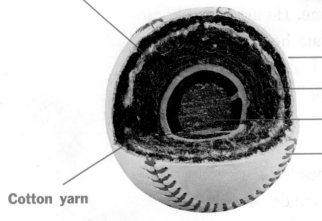

Cowhide

Gray wool yarn

Cork and rubber center

108 stitches done by hand

Cotton yarn

Want to Make a Baseball?

Wrap a round piece of cork with 150 yards of cotton yarn and 219 yards of wool yarn. Cover it with cowhide. Sew it with 108 stitches. You've got yourself a baseball!

FIND OUT MORE

Visit our website:

www.mhschool.com/tfk

*inter*NET
CONNECTION

Based on an article in *TIME FOR KIDS*.

Story Questions & Activities

1. Where was the team that won the 1998 Little League World Series from?

2. How do you think Chris Cardone felt when he hit his second home run?

3. Do you think the town celebration focused on the heroes of the final game or on the entire team? Explain.

4. What is the main idea of this selection?

5. Austin Healy and Todd Frazier both got souvenir baseballs. What makes their baseballs so special to them?

Write an Essay

Think about your favorite sport or hobby. Was there a time when you had a great game or made something that you were proud of? Write an essay telling what you did and why it made you feel good.

Make a Bar Graph

Borrow a baseball or a softball. In a clear area outside, throw the ball underhand three times. Stand at the same spot each time. Measure and record the distance you were able to throw the ball each time. Make a bar graph to show your data.

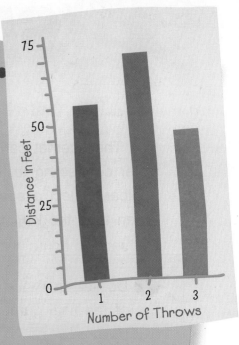

Draw a Map

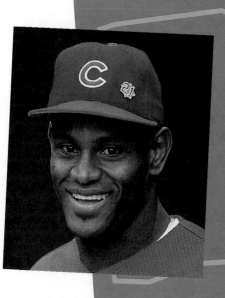

In 1998, Sammy Sosa hit 66 home runs. He is from the Dominican Republic, an island in the Caribbean. Make a map of the Dominican Republic and include some facts about the island.

Find Out More

Who invented baseball? Basketball? Soccer? Pick your favorite sport and find out when and where people first began playing it. Make a poster about your sport.

Use a Search Engine

The Internet can be used to search for almost anything. After connecting to the Internet, click on **Search** in the toolbar. Select a **search engine** by typing the name of one. Then type the key words for the subject you are researching.

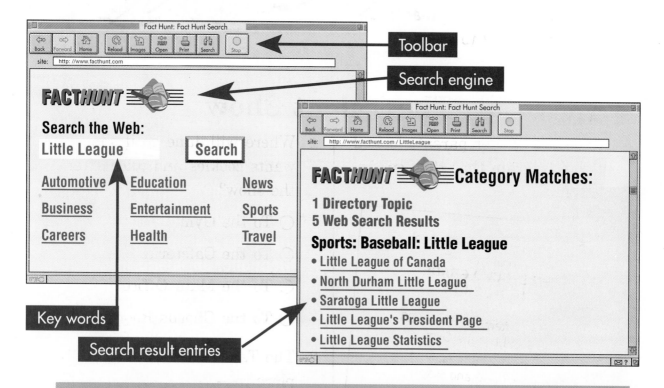

Use the computer screens to answer these questions.

1 Which search engine was chosen?

2 What key words were used for the search?

3 How many search result entries were found?

4 Which search result entry might you click on to find out more about the Little League batting averages?

5 How could you change the search to find information on the winners of the 1998 Little League World Series?

DIRECTIONS:
Read the story. Then read each
question about the story.

SAMPLE

The Talent Show

June and her parents looked at the program that they got in the mail.

> Churchill Elementary School
> presents
> **THE SECOND GRADE
> TALENT SHOW**
>
> Saturday afternoon, March 23
> 3:30 PM, in the Gym
>
> **Performances:**
> Taka Smith—Piano Playing
> James Mason—Poem
> Alesha Botts—Tap Dance
> Chorus—America the Beautiful
> Cookies and juice will be served in the
> Cafeteria after the performance.
>
> **Special thanks to:**
> Mr. George Mendez, our teacher
> Lisa Miller, school custodian
> All of our family and friends

1 Where will June go if she wants cookies and juice after the show?

○ To the Gym

○ To the Cafeteria

○ To the Main Office

○ To the Chorus Room

2 The Talent Show will take place in—

○ the Gym

○ the Cafeteria

○ the Main Office

○ the Chorus Room

Why are your
answers correct?

Abuelita's Lap

I know a place where I can sit
and tell about my day,
tell every color that I saw
from green to cactus gray.

I know a place where I can sit
and hear a favorite beat,
her heart and *cuentos* from the past,
the rhythms honey-sweet.

I know a place where I can sit
and listen to a star,
listen to its silent song
gliding from afar.

I know a place where I can sit
and hear the wind go by,
hearing it spinning round my house,
my whirling lullaby.

by Pat Mora

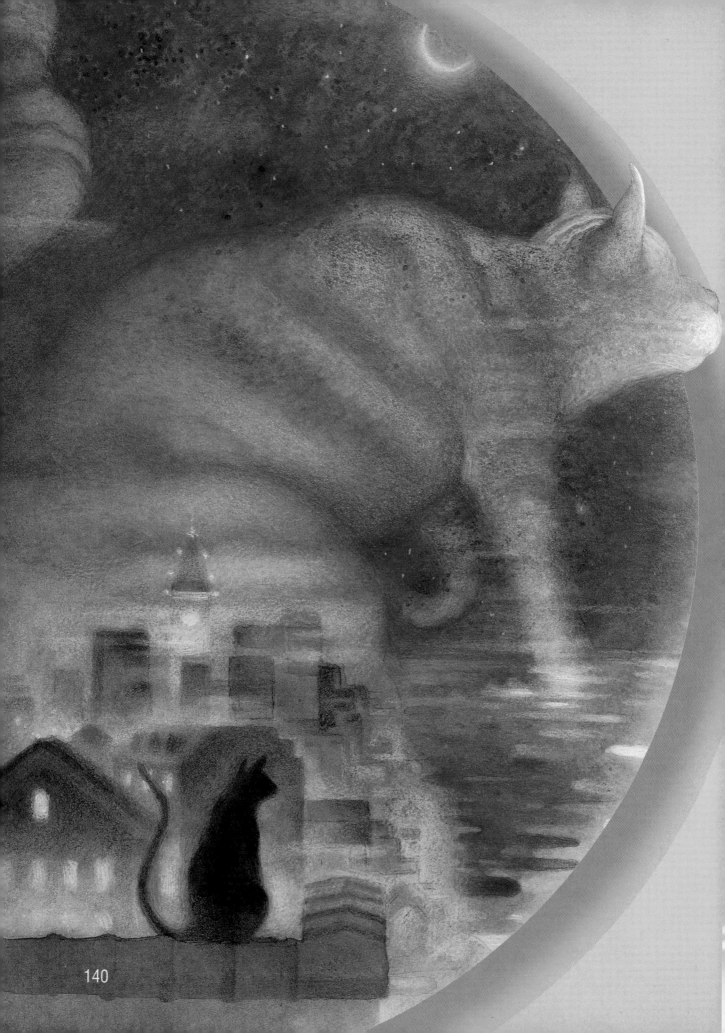

Nature Links

Fog

The fog comes
on little cat feet.

It sits looking
over harbor and city
on silent haunches
and then moves on.

by Carl Sandburg

Stories in Art

Murals are usually painted in a public place for everyone to enjoy. Often members of a community work together to paint a mural.

Look at this mural. What can you tell about it? What might have happened to make the people hug the city? How do you think the artist who painted the mural feels about his community?

Look again at the painting. What is the most unusual thing about it? Why?

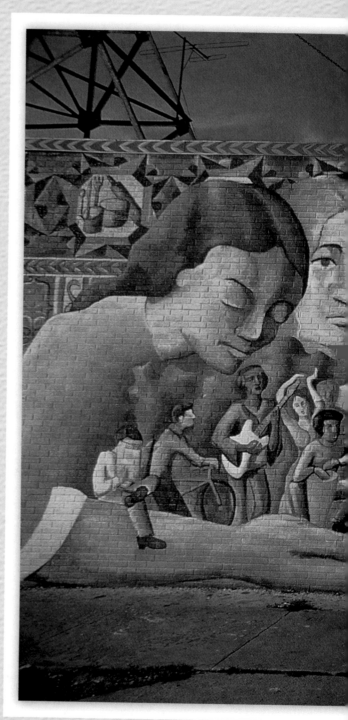

Together Protect the Community
by John Pitman Weber, 1976
Located on Diversity Street, Chicago

Meet DyAnne DiSalvo-Ryan

As a child, DyAnne DiSalvo-Ryan drew all the time. She recalls, "I always loved a sharp pencil and a new piece of paper." People would ask if she wanted to be an artist someday. She'd say, "I'm an artist already."

DiSalvo-Ryan hopes her drawings will feel familiar to children. She wants them "to be able to see themselves or their neighbors" in her art.

DiSalvo-Ryan's stories often grow out of her own experiences. *Uncle Willie and the Soup Kitchen* is based on her volunteer work at a soup kitchen. The garden lot she always passed on the way there inspired *City Green*.

CITY GREEN

by DyAnne DiSalvo-Ryan

There used to be a building right here on this lot. It was three floors up and down, an empty building nailed up shut for as long as I could remember. My friend Miss Rosa told me Old Man Hammer used to live there—some other neighbors too. But when I asked him about that, he only hollered, "Scram."

Old Man Hammer, hard as nails.

Last year two people from the city came by, dressed in suits and holding papers. They said, "This building is unsafe. It will have to be torn down."

By winter a crane with a wrecking ball was parked outside. Mama gathered everyone to watch from our front window. In three slow blows that building was knocked into a heap of pieces. Then workers took the rubble away in a truck and filled the hole with dirt.

Now this block looks like a big smile with one tooth missing. Old Man Hammer sits on his stoop and shakes his head. "Look at that piece of junk land on a city block," Old Man Hammer says. "Once that building could've been saved. But nobody even tried."

And every day when I pass this lot it makes me sad to see it. Every single day.

Then spring comes, and right on schedule Miss Rosa starts cleaning her coffee cans. Miss Rosa and I keep coffee cans outside our windowsills. Every year we buy two packets of seeds at the hardware store—sometimes marigolds, sometimes zinnias, and one time we tried tomatoes. We go to the park, scoop some dirt, and fill up the cans halfway.

This time Old Man Hammer stops us on the way to the park. "This good for nothin' lot has plenty of dirt right here," he says.

Then all at once I look at Miss Rosa. And she is smiling back at me. "A *lot* of dirt," Miss Rosa says.

"Like one big coffee can," I say.

That's when we decide to do something about this lot.

Quick as a wink I'm digging away, already thinking of gardens and flowers. But Old Man Hammer shakes his finger. "You can't dig more dirt than that. This lot is city property."

Miss Rosa and I go to see Mr. Bennett. He used to work for the city. "I seem to remember a program," he says, "that lets people rent empty lots."

That's how Miss Rosa and I form a group of people from our block. We pass around a petition that says: WE WANT TO LEASE THIS LOT. In less than a week we have plenty of names.

"Sign with us?" I ask Old Man Hammer.

"I'm not signin' nothin'," he says. "And nothin' is what's gonna happen."

But something did.

The next week, a bunch of us take a bus to city hall. We walk up the steps to the proper office and hand the woman our list. She checks her files and types some notes and makes some copies. "That will be one dollar, please."

We rent the lot from the city that day. It was just as simple as that.

Saturday morning I'm up with the sun and looking at this lot. My mama looks out too. "Marcy," she says, and hugs me close. "Today I'm helping you and Rosa."

After shopping, Mama empties her grocery bags and folds them flat to carry under her arm. "Come on, Mrs. B.," Mama tells her friend. "We're going to clear this lot."

Then what do you know but my brother comes along. My brother is tall and strong. At first, he scratches his neck and shakes his head just like Old Man Hammer. But Mama smiles and says, "None of that here!" So all day long he piles junk in those bags and carries them to the curb.

Now, this time of day is early. Neighbors pass by and see what we're doing. Most say, "We want to help too." They have a little time to spare. Then this one calls that one and that one calls another.

"Come on and help," I call to Old Man Hammer.

"I'm not helpin' nobody," he hollers. "You're all wastin' your time."

Sour grapes my mama'd say, and sour grapes is right.

Just before supper, when we are good and hungry, my mama looks around this lot. "Marcy," she says, "you're making something happen here."

Next day the city drops off tools like rakes and brooms, and a Dumpster for trash. Now there's even more neighbors to help. Miss Rosa, my brother, and I say "Good morning" to Old Man Hammer, but Old Man Hammer just waves like he's swatting a fly.

"Why is Old Man Hammer so mean and cranky these days?" my brother asks.

"Maybe he's really sad," I tell him. "Maybe he misses his building."

"That rotten old building?" My brother shrugs. "He should be happy the city tore down that mess."

"Give him time," Miss Rosa says. "Good things take time."

Mr. Bennett brings wood—old slats he's saved—and nails in a cup. "I knew all along I saved them for something," he says. "This wood's good wood."

Then Mr. Rocco from two houses down comes, carrying two cans of paint. "I'll never use these," he says. "The color's too bright. But here, this lot could use some brightening up."

Well, anyone can tell with all the excitement that something is going on. And everyone has an idea about what to plant—strawberries, carrots, lettuce, and more. Tulips and daisies, petunias, and more! Sonny turns the dirt over with a snow shovel. Even Leslie's baby tries to dig with a spoon.

For lunch, Miss Rosa brings milk and jelly and bread and spreads a beach towel where the junk is cleared. By the end of the day a fence is built and painted as bright as the sun.

Later, Mama kisses my cheek and closes my bedroom door. By the streetlights I see Old Man Hammer come down his steps to open the gate and walk to the back of this lot. He bends down quick, sprinkling something from his pocket and covering it over with dirt.

In the morning I tell my brother. "Oh, Marcy," he says. "You're dreaming. You're wishing too hard."

But I know what I saw, and I tell my mama, "Old Man Hammer's planted some seeds."

Right after breakfast, I walk to the back of this lot. And there it is—a tiny raised bed of soil. It is neat and tidy, just like the rows we've planted. Now I know for sure that Old Man Hammer planted something. So I pat the soil for good luck and make a little fence to keep the seeds safe.

Every day I go for a look inside our garden lot. Other neighbors stop in too. One day Mrs. Wells comes by. "This is right where my grandmother's bedroom used to be," she says. "That's why I planted my flowers there."

I feel sad when I hear that. With all the digging and planting and weeding and watering, I'd forgotten about the building that had been on this lot. Old Man Hammer had lived there too. I go to the back, where he planted his seeds. I wonder if this was the place where his room used to be.

I look down. Beside my feet, some tiny stems are sprouting. Old Man Hammer's seeds have grown! I run to his stoop. "Come with me!" I beg, tugging at his hand. "You'll want to see."

I walk him past the hollyhocks, the daisies, the peppers, the rows of lettuce. I show him the strawberries that I planted. When Old Man Hammer sees his little garden bed, his sour grapes turn sweet. "Marcy, child." He shakes his head. "This lot was good for nothin'. Now it's nothin' but good," he says.

Soon summertime comes, and this lot really grows. It fills with vegetables, herbs, and flowers. And way in the back, taller than anything else, is a beautiful patch of yellow sunflowers. Old Man Hammer comes every day. He sits in the sun, eats his lunch, and sometimes comes back with supper.

Nobody knows how the sunflowers came—not Leslie, my brother, or Miss Rosa. Not Mr. Bennett, or Sonny, or anyone else. But Old Man Hammer just sits there smiling at me. We know whose flowers they are.

Starting a Community Garden

All across America people have joined together to turn ugly lots into beautiful gardens. You may not imagine that you can do it—but you *can*. If there is already a community garden in your neighborhood, ask your neighbors how they got started. But if you are the first on your block to "make something happen," this is what you can do:

1. Find an interested grown-up who wants to help you: a parent or guardian, a teacher, a librarian, or a neighbor.

2. Find out the address of the lot. This is very important. You may have to talk to neighbors or look at the address of the buildings next door. Example: The lot I am interested in is on Main Street. It is between 75 Main Street and 81 Main Street.

3. While you are finding out the address of the lot, get in touch with the local gardening program in your area (see end of this note). Say that you are interested in starting a garden. Since every city is different, your local program will be able to steer you in the right direction.

4. Find out who the owner is. The Department of Records at your local city hall can help. Look in the telephone book for the address of city hall in your area.

5. If the lot is owned by the city, the people at city hall can help you get permission to use the lot. Usually there is a small fee. If the lot is owned by an individual person or group, you will need to get permission from that person or group to use the lot.

6. Once you get permission to use the lot, it's yours to name!

There are hundreds of gardening programs that are ready to help community gardeners with information, soil, seeds, fencing, and more.

To find out the community gardening program that is nearest you, write to:

American Community Gardening Association
325 Walnut Street
Philadelphia, PA 19106

Community gardens bring people together. Join the work and join the fun!

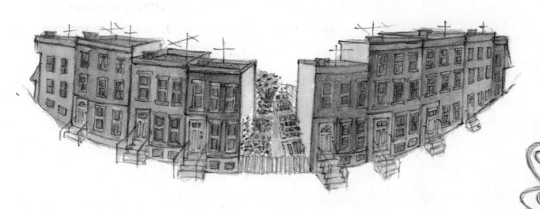

Story Questions & Activities

1. What did the lot look like at the beginning of the story?

2. Why was Old Man Hammer so upset about the building that was torn down?

3. Do you think the people on the block will plant the garden again next year? Why or why not?

4. What is this story mainly about?

5. If Old Man Hammer met the grandfather from "Grandfather's Journey," how would they get along? What might they talk about?

Write a Plan

Write a plan for a neighborhood garden. Explain how neighbors should choose a place, prepare it, and decide what to plant there. Check that your plan seems logical and well-organized.

Design a Garden

Think about the kind of garden you would like to have. What shape would your garden be? Would you plant flowers, vegetables, or both? Draw and label a design for the garden.

Make a Speech

Brainstorm some ways that you, like Marcy, could make your environment better. Think of a project that would improve your school, home, or community. Prepare a speech about your project. Explain why other people should help, too.

Find Out More

Start a garden right in your classroom! First find out what plants grow well indoors. Choose one plant. Then find out what you can do to help the plant grow. Does it need sun or shade? How often should you water it?

STUDY SKILLS

Use a Telephone Directory

In "City Green," neighbors work together to create something beautiful. People working together on a project often need to call each other. A telephone directory gives the names, addresses, and phone numbers of people and businesses in an area.

TELEPHONE DIRECTORY

128 PHOTO—POLLARD

Photo Phinishers 12 Beltway...........................555-4235	Pittman Gale 64 River St.................................555-6987
Phung Yan Chu 16 Center Ave 555-0971	Pittman Roger MD
PHYLLIS'S PET SHOP	1245 Santa Ana Blvd.........555-9898
1166 Park Hwy **555-8920**	Pitts Loleta 133 Allen Way 555-6348
Pickard Nell 18 Dysart Ave............................555-5681	Pizel John 501 Whitney Ave 555-6324
Pickard Roberto 9 Day St................................555-6514	**PLAINVILLE BOAT SHOP**
Pickett Ana 809 Buena Vista 555-8942	1621 Park Hwy.................**555-9852**
Picovsky Susan 62 Wood St 555-6574	Plante Kevan 113 River St...............................555-7421
Pidgeon C G 920 Main St.................................555-9821	Plante Sylvia 113 River St................................555-7871
Pie & Cake Co 622 Park Hwy 555-6355	Pletcher Arlen 75 Wood St.............................555-6314
Piedra Bill 51 Horace St 555-3531	Plumisto LeRoy 441 River St...........................555-6387
Piedras Mike 23 Stuart Ave 555-6584	Plummar David 35 Main St 555-6871
Piedras J........ ......Ave....... 555-7435	....573 Woodlawn Ave......... ...58

Use the telephone directory to answer these questions.

1 What are Sylvia Plante's address and telephone number?

2 What is Mr. Pickard's first name?

3 Where would you go if you wanted to buy a canary?

4 On what street is the Plainville Boat Shop?

5 Why is a telephone directory useful?

DIRECTIONS:

Read the story. Then read each question about the story.

SAMPLE

The Important Meeting

Jack's mother paused at the front door. "Do you have your key to the house, Jack?" she asked. "My meeting might run late this afternoon. I might not be home when school gets out."

Jack smiled and nodded. "Don't worry, Mom," he said. "I have it. You go ahead—don't be late!"

Jack's mother had opened her own gas station five years ago. He knew that the meeting today was important to her. She was meeting with the banker to open a new gas station.

"Don't forget your briefcase, Mom," Jack reminded her.

"Thanks, Jack," his mother called. "See you tonight! Wish me luck!"

1 Why might Jack's mother come home late?

○ She had a flat tire.

○ She did not have a key.

○ She had a meeting.

○ She had to work.

2 How did Jack feel about his mother's business?

○ Worried

○ Angry

○ Hopeful

○ Confused

Why are your answers correct?

Some paintings are full of action. You can almost feel, smell, and hear what is happening. The artist makes you feel like you are there.

Look at the painting. What can you tell about it? Pretend that the artist painted the volcano the morning after it erupted. How would the painting look different? How would it look the same?

Why do you think the artist painted the volcano erupting at night? Explain your reasons.

Naples: Vesuvius Erupting, 22nd October 1822

The Sun, the Wind

by Lisa Westberg Peters
Illustrated by Ted Rand

and the Rain

This is the story of two mountains. The earth made one. Elizabeth in her yellow sun hat made the other.

The earth made its mountain millions of years ago.
It began as a pool underground, first fiery hot and soft,
then cold and rock-hard.

Elizabeth made hers on the beach today with
bucketsful of wet sand.

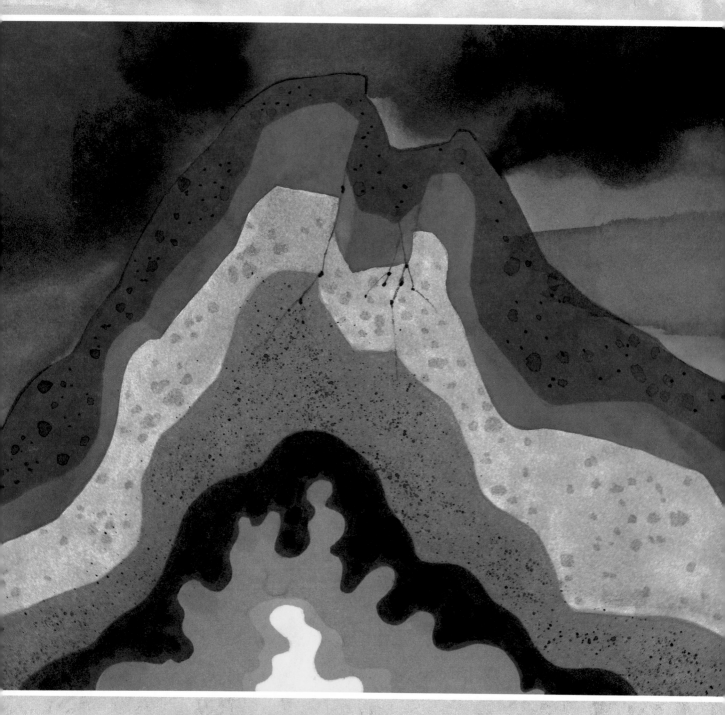

Eons passed. The earth cracked and shifted until
the rock of its mountain slowly rose.

Elizabeth quickly piled her sand high. She patted it smooth all the way around.

The earth mountain sparkled against the sky.
Furry animals walked in its lush green valleys.

Elizabeth's mountain stood almost as tall as she,
with twigs for trees and pebbles for animals. Elizabeth
was proud of her fine sand mountain.

The sun beat down, day after day, year after year,
on the earth mountain's sharp peaks. The wind howled
through its canyons.

Elizabeth's mountain baked in the afternoon heat.
The breeze loosened a few grains of sand and blew them
into Elizabeth's eyes and hair.

Countless rainstorms pounded the earth mountain.
The water seeped into its rocks, making them crumble,
then tumble into small streams.

An afternoon shower blew in suddenly and Elizabeth
watched as the water began to destroy the mountain
she had worked so hard to build. Her tears fell as freely
as the rain.

The small streams rushed together to become a
raging river. The river gouged a deep valley. It ground
the earth mountain's rough rocks into smooth pebbles.

Elizabeth could see the rain carving little valleys
into her mountain. Tiny rivers carried the sand down
the beach.

As the river flowed away from the earth mountain, it ground pebbles into sand and dumped the sand on a broad plain. Then it emptied into the sea.

Elizabeth saw the sand from her mountain spread
silently into small fans. She wiped away her tears.

In just a blink of earth time, the earth mountain
traded rocks for sand, jagged peaks for flat layers.

After a few minutes, the shower was over. Elizabeth's mountain was just a bump on the beach.

The thick and heavy layers of sand sank down, down, down into the earth until they were squeezed into layers of sandstone.

Elizabeth scooped up a handful of sand from one of the small fans on the beach. She smiled. It was wet and hard—just right. This time she hurried, for the sun was dropping in the sky.

The earth cracked and shifted again. Bending and breaking, the sandstone layers slowly rose to become a new mountain.

Elizabeth finished her new sand mountain. She
brushed sand off her hands, picked up her bucket, and
walked back up the beach.

Elizabeth is walking on the new earth mountain.
She steps carefully up the steep path from the beach.
When she stops to rest, she sees a smooth mound
of sand far below. It looks very small.

As she turns to leave, Elizabeth reaches out to
touch the sandstone wall. Tiny grains of sand fall on
her shoulders.

She brushes them off and watches them fall to the
ground, where they will stay for just a while...
in the sun, the wind and the rain.

Meet
Lisa Westberg Peters

Lisa Westberg Peters wanted to write a book for children that would explain geology and how mountains change over time.

"I was lucky enough to take some good geology courses and several unforgettable trips into the mountains," she said. Then she visited a mountain along the coast in Washington State and wrote the story that became *The Sun, the Wind and the Rain.*

Meet
Ted Rand

Ted Rand says the mountain painted on the cover of *The Sun, the Wind and the Rain* is Mt. Rainier in the Cascade Range in Washington State. He says that the beach and shoreline are very much like those on Puget Sound and along the Pacific Coast.

"I'd like to encourage young readers to draw and enjoy the fun of it. Drawing is a second language to me, and I hope it becomes that to you," Mr. Rand says.

199

Story Questions & Activities

1. What does Elizabeth do after the rain washes away her mountain?

2. How was the way Elizabeth made her mountain different from the way Earth made its mountain?

3. Why is "The Sun, the Wind and the Rain" a good title for this selection?

4. What is the main idea of this selection?

5. How are Elizabeth and Marcy from "City Green" alike or different?

Write an Essay

Write an essay that tells how a rainstorm or snowstorm changes a place. Choose a place you know well, such as your backyard or a playing field. Use lively, descriptive words.

Check for Weathering

The sun, wind, rain, and ice can cause things to become dried, worn, cracked, or faded. This process is called **weathering**. With an adult, go outside and look for signs of weathering. Look at buildings. Look at streets. Look at sidewalks. List different examples of weathering that you find.

Paint with Sand

On a poster, draw the layers of a mountain. Choose a different color of sand for each layer. Then cover one layer on the poster with glue. Sprinkle colored sand over the glue. Shake off any extra sand. Then do the same for each of the other layers.

Find Out More

Now that you know how mountains are formed, you may want to find out more about mountains in your area. What are the closest mountains to where you live? What is the tallest mountain in your state? In the country?

Use a Dictionary

When you are reading a science selection such as "The Sun, the Wind and the Rain," it helps to keep a dictionary handy. You can use the dictionary to look up the spelling, meaning, or pronunciation of words.

---

geology/gerbil

geology The science that deals with the structure and physical changes of the earth or other planets that are mostly made of rocks.
ge•ol•o•gy (jē ol′ ə jē) *noun, plural* **geologies.**

geometry The branch of mathematics that deals with the measurement and relation of points, lines, angles, plane figures, and solids.
ge•om•e•try (jē om′ i trē) *noun, plural* **geometries.**

Georgia A state in the southeastern United States. Its capital is Atlanta.
Geor•gia (jôr′ jə) *noun.*

geranium A plant with bright red, pink, white, or lavender flowers. The leaves of some geraniums have a scent.
ge•ra•ni•um (jə rā′ nē əm) *noun, plural* **geraniums.**

gerbil A small rodent that is native to deserts in Africa and Asia. It lives in a burrow and is sometimes kept as a pet.
ger•bil (jûr′ bil) *noun, plural* **gerbils.**

Use the dictionary page to answer these questions.

1 What does the word *geology* mean?

2 Is *geranium* an adjective or noun?

3 If you want to know how to say the word *gerbil*, what should you do?

4 What is the last word on the page? How do you know?

5 Entries for the words *portrait* and *pose* appear on a later page. Which entry would come first?

Test Tip
As you read the story, think about what the characters are doing.

DIRECTIONS:
Read the story. Then read each question about the story.

SAMPLE

Reggie's Flat Tire

Officer Brown saw that Reggie had a big frown, so he asked him what was wrong.

"My bike has a flat tire," Reggie said. "It won't hold air anymore."

Officer Brown smiled and went to his police car. He had a tire-patch kit in the car for emergencies. He got the kit out and looked at Reggie's tire.

"It looks like you rode over a tack," he said. "See this hole? It's tiny, but that is where your tire is losing air."

"Can it be fixed?" Reggie asked. He was nervous because he did not have enough money for a new tire.

"Oh, yes," Officer Brown said. "Would you please hand me that roll of patch tape? I will fix your tire."

1 How did Reggie feel about getting a new tire?

○ Happy

○ Worried

○ Excited

○ Lonely

2 Who was going to fix the bicycle tire?

○ Reggie

○ Officer Brown

○ Reggie's mother

○ The repairman

Stories in Art

Some paintings tell part of a story. You can see what is happening, but you might wonder what caused it.

Look at this painting. What is happening? What do you think happened to make the dog carry a suitcase? What might happen next?

Look at the painting again. How does it make you feel? Why?

Family Going Shopping
by Aaron Birnbaum, 1993

Dream Wolf

by Paul Goble

In the old days the people travelled over the plains. They followed the great herds of buffalo.

Every year when the berries were ripe, they would leave the plains and go up into the hills. They made camp in a valley where the berry bushes grow. Everyone picked great quantities. They mashed the berries into little cakes which they dried in the sun. These they stored in painted bags for the winter.

Tiblo (tee-blow) was too young to play with the older boys. He and his little sister, Tanksi (tawnk-she), had to go berry-picking with their mother and the other women and children.

iblo was soon tired of picking, and too full to eat any more. When nobody was looking he slipped away with Tanksi to climb the hills.

They climbed up and up among the rocks and cedar trees where bighorn sheep and bears live. Soon they could hardly hear the berry-pickers laughing and calling to each other far below. Tiblo wanted to reach the top. They climbed on.

They never noticed the sun starting to go down behind the hills.

It was getting dark when Tiblo knew they had to go back home. In the twilight every hill and valley looked the same. He did not know which way to go. He called out. . . . Only the echoes answered him.

209

They wandered on. Tiblo was lost. Darkness closed around them. It grew colder. They were tired and hungry, and Tanksi began to cry.

Speaking of happy things, Tiblo found a small cave among the rocks. They crawled inside to shelter for the night.

The children were tired, and in a little while they fell asleep. Tiblo had a dream.

He dreamed that a wolf with shining eyes entered the cave. In his dream he felt the wolf's hot breath and its rough tongue licking his face. The wolf lay down beside him. His shaggy fur was like a blanket which kept Tiblo and Tanksi warm.

The sun was already shining into the mouth of the cave when Tiblo opened his eyes again.

Tiblo woke up his sister. They crawled out of the cave into the warm sunshine. He took Tanksi by the hand, and they set off walking down the hill.

When the children came to a stream, they stopped to drink. Suddenly Tiblo saw that a wolf was sitting on some rocks close by, watching them. At once he remembered his dream.

"O Wolf," Tiblo said, "we are lost. Mother will be crying. Help us to find our way home again."

The wolf panted and smiled. "My children, do not worry. I will help you. Last night you slept in my den. Follow me now, and I will take you home."

The wolf trotted off. He looked back to see that the children were following. From time to time he trotted ahead out of sight, but he always returned.

At last the wolf led them to a hilltop. The children were filled with joy to see their home in the valley below. The wolf sat back on his haunches and smiled. And then he trotted off back toward the hills. The children begged him to come and live with them.

"No," the wolf called back, "I like to wander from place to place with my friends. Listen for me in the evenings! You will hear me calling, and you will know that I never forget you."

People in the camp saw the children coming down the hill. The men jumped on to their horses, and galloped out to bring them home. Everyone was happy that the children were safe.

Tiblo told how the wolf had brought them home. Everyone walked into the hills to thank the wolf. They spread a blanket for him to sit on. They gave him necklaces and other beautiful gifts.

There has been close kinship with the Wolf People for as long as anyone can remember. That is what they say.

The wolves are no longer heard calling
in the evenings at berry-picking time. Hunters
have killed and driven them away with guns
and traps and poisons. People say that the
wolves will return when we, like Tiblo and
Tanksi, have the wolves in our hearts and
dreams again.

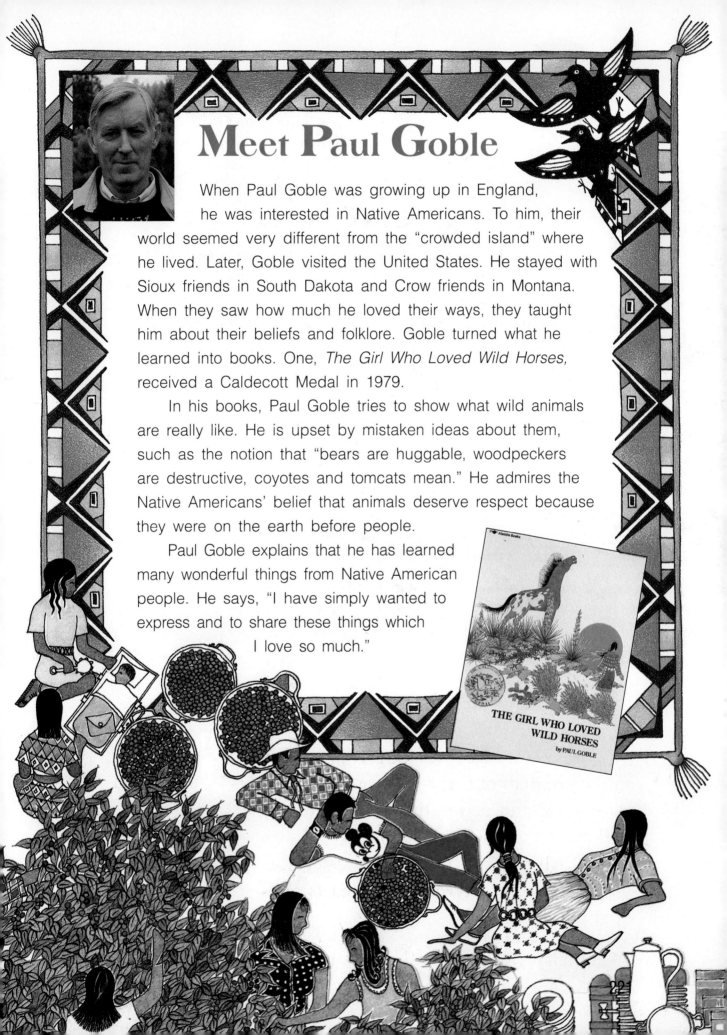

Meet Paul Goble

When Paul Goble was growing up in England, he was interested in Native Americans. To him, their world seemed very different from the "crowded island" where he lived. Later, Goble visited the United States. He stayed with Sioux friends in South Dakota and Crow friends in Montana. When they saw how much he loved their ways, they taught him about their beliefs and folklore. Goble turned what he learned into books. One, *The Girl Who Loved Wild Horses,* received a Caldecott Medal in 1979.

In his books, Paul Goble tries to show what wild animals are really like. He is upset by mistaken ideas about them, such as the notion that "bears are huggable, woodpeckers are destructive, coyotes and tomcats mean." He admires the Native Americans' belief that animals deserve respect because they were on the earth before people.

Paul Goble explains that he has learned many wonderful things from Native American people. He says, "I have simply wanted to express and to share these things which I love so much."

THE GIRL WHO LOVED
WILD HORSES
by PAUL GOBLE

Story Questions & Activities

1. What were Tiblo and Tanksi doing when they got lost?

2. How did Tiblo's dream help the two children get home? Explain.

3. Legends often explain why things are the way they are. What might this legend explain?

4. What is this story mostly about?

5. How is the wolf in this story different from wolves in other stories that you know?

Write Directions

Pretend you are the wolf in the story. Write directions for Tiblo and Tanksi to get home. Should they turn right at a big rock? Left at a stream? Be sure to give the directions in a clear, simple order.

Draw Pictures

Pretend that a wolf goes to visit a skunk. What might be fun about the visit? What might some problems be? Draw a series of pictures showing what might happen. Write a caption for each picture.

Make a Map

Find out which part of the United States is called the Great Plains. Trace a map of the United States, label each state, and then shade in the area that makes up the Great Plains.

Find Out More

Did you know that some kinds of wild animals, such as wolves, live in groups but others do not? Research three different types of animals that live in groups. Also find out what the group is called. For example, a group of wolves is called a pack.

223

Use an Encyclopedia

An encyclopedia is a set of books that contains information on many subjects. Each book within the set is called a volume. The volumes are arranged in alphabetical order. So are the entries inside each volume.

Sioux Falls College, *See under* SCHOOLS, COLLEGES, AND UNIVERSITIES.

Sioux Indians, the popular name of a large tribe of North American Indians who lived in North Dakota, South Dakota, Nebraska, Montana, and Wyoming. Calling themselves the Dakota, they were known as the Sioux, after a French name given them. They were divided into the Santee, Yankton, and Teton groups.

Like other Plains Indians, the Sioux hunted buffalo, which provided them with food, hides for clothing and teepees, and bone and horn for implements.

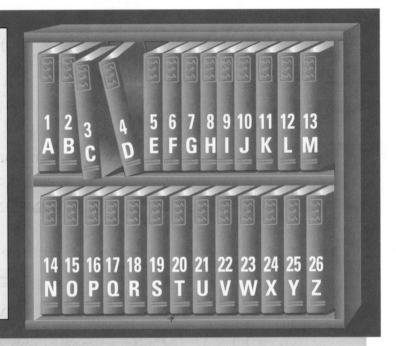

Use the set of encyclopedias and the sample entries to answer these questions.

1 How many volumes are in this set of encyclopedias?

2 In which volume will you find an entry called "Sioux Indians"?

3 What are the two entries shown in the sample?

4 What are four states where the Sioux lived?

5 For more information on Sioux Falls College, what is another entry that you should check in this set of encyclopedias?

TEST POWER

DIRECTIONS:
Read the story. Then read each question about the story.

SAMPLE

The Polar Bear Club

In some parts of the country, groups of people celebrate the New Year in a special way. In towns near the ocean, people go for a swim in the freezing cold water on the first day in January! One of these groups of people is called the Polar Bear Club.

All kinds of people are members of the Polar Bear Club. They swim in the ocean even in the middle of the winter!

"There's nothing as fun as freezing water filled with warm hearts," says Joe Cabona. "I don't stay in for long," Joe says. "But I stay in long enough to celebrate the New Year. Then my friends and I all go over to

someone's house and drink hot apple cider. It's a special <u>occasion</u>!"

1 In this story, the word <u>occasion</u> means—

   ○ water

   ○ heart

   ○ person

   ○ event

2 Why do the Polar Bear Club members swim in the ocean in January?

   ○ To celebrate the New Year

   ○ They like cold water

   ○ So they can catch a cold

   ○ To warm their hearts

Stories in Art

Many animals have special features that help them get the food they need. A garden spider spins a web to catch its food. A harvester ant has strong jaws that help it chew seeds.

Look at the painting. What can you tell about this hummingbird? How will its bill help it to sip nectar from the flowers? What details do you notice about the flowers?

Look at the painting again. What do you think are the important details in the picture?

Ruby-Throat & Columbine
by Robert Bateman, 1983

Meet Diane Hoyt-Goldsmith

Diane Hoyt-Goldsmith grew up in Oregon and has always loved to read. She received a Fine Arts degree from Pratt Institute in New York City, and worked in New York as a book designer for many years. When she moved to California in 1979, she started Square Moon Productions, where she is now the art director.

In 1990, Ms. Hoyt-Goldsmith published her first book, *Totem Pole.* Since that time, she has written many award-winning books about children from different cultures in the United States and around the world.

Ms. Hoyt-Goldsmith still loves to read. She is also a gardener and art collector. She lives with her family in Orinda, California.

Spiders at Work

by Diane Hoyt-Goldsmith

Nature's Web Maker

The tiny creature called a spider spins a web that is both beautiful and useful. Although it looks like lace, the web is a deadly trap.

Hanging in the space between two plants, the threads that make up the web are almost invisible. A fly buzzes into the web and gets stuck. Then the spider runs out and wraps the insect up in sticky threads. Next the spider carries the fly away to eat it.

The garden spider is one of nature's best builders. Let's look at how it makes its web between two plants.

First, the spider makes a bridge line by spinning out a long silk thread. The silk begins as a liquid that the spider sprays from its body. When the silk hits the air, it hardens into the strongest fiber found in nature.

Air currents blow one end of this thread to another plant where it sticks. The spider travels along the bridge line it has made. It drops another line down to a plant below and travels down it. Then it comes back up with another silk thread to make a triangle. The spider keeps spinning. Back and forth, up and down, the spider goes. The web now looks something like the spokes of a wheel. Then the spider lays the trap— a long thread of sticky silk that spirals around the spokes until it reaches the center of the wheel. When the spider gets a victim, it can race down the spokes because they are dry, not sticky, and capture its prey.

Spiders, Spiders, Everywhere

There are many different kinds of spiders. Some spiders make webs to catch their food in the air. Others hunt for insects on the ground.

Spiders can be found anywhere on Earth. They live in jungles near the sea. They live on the top of the highest mountains. Because spiders travel by clinging to wind-blown silk threads (a kind of travel called ballooning), they have also been found miles up in the sky and hundreds of miles out to sea.

Spiders come in many sizes. Some are as small as the head of a pin. A few are much larger. The bird eating tarantulas of South America can be as long as ten inches with their legs spread.

There are more than 30,000 species of spiders living in the world—that we know about. Scientists believe the total number of kinds of spiders may be anywhere from 50,000 to 100,000. More than 2,000 different kinds of spiders live in the United States. Two of the best-known are the black widow spider and the tarantula.

The Dangerous Black Widow

The female black widow has a poisonous bite that can cause humans serious illness and even death. But the black widow is even more dangerous to her mate. From time to time she kills and eats him. This behavior isn't unusual among spiders— many other kinds do the same thing.

Black widows have a small, shiny black body. On the bottom there is a red or yellow mark shaped like an hourglass. Black widows can be found everywhere in the United States except Alaska.

The poison in the black widow's bite is very strong. The spider uses it to kill the insects it eats. The black widow makes a web to catch an insect. When she has one in her trap, she throws a few sticky threads over it. As the insect struggles to get free, the black widow bites and kills it. Then she can eat it whenever she wants to.

The poison in the bite of the black widow spider is more deadly than the venom of a rattlesnake.

The bird spider tarantula of South America lives in trees and eats small birds.

Tarantulas have lived on Earth since the time of the dinosaurs.

Most spiders live only for a year or so. Female tarantulas, however, can live to be 35 years old or more.

Black widow spiders do not bite people very often. If the spider is left alone, it won't hurt anyone. The best advice is to avoid any spider with a shiny, black body and a red or yellow mark on the bottom.

Tarantulas— Deadly Monsters?

Most tarantulas aren't very dangerous, but they look like they are! Unlike other spiders, the tarantula can be huge—anywhere from the size of a quarter to the size of an outstretched human hand. Its body is covered with hair.

Although tarantulas look like monsters, most kinds have a bite no more powerful than a bee sting. The tarantula likes to be left alone in a quiet, dark place. In fact, some people think that tarantulas make good pets.

The hairs on the tarantula's body help it to defend itself. When in danger, the tarantula drops some of its hairs. Each hair has a tiny barb at the end. This barb is as sharp as a fish hook and can hurt the skin and eyes of an enemy.

These hairs also pose the spider's greatest threat to humans, because they can cause an allergic reaction in some people.

Although tarantulas have eight eyes, they can't see very well. They hide and wait for an insect to come to them. The hairs on the tarantula's body and legs help it to sense when something is getting close. The tarantula feeds on all kinds of beetles, grasshoppers, and caterpillars.

The Daddy-longlegs

Certain creatures that we may think are spiders are not. Daddy-longlegs are a good example of this. They look like spiders because they are part of the same family. Like many spiders, daddy-longlegs are helpful to humans. They eat insects that are harmful. For example, they like to eat grasshoppers and locusts—insects that can ruin a farmer's crops. They also like to eat flies and mosquitoes. These insects spread sickness to humans.

Can you guess how the daddy-longlegs got its name? It has very long legs. Two of its legs are even longer than all the others.

These two legs have a special purpose. The daddy-longlegs uses them to touch things as it passes. The fine hairs on these legs help it to hear. There are also dark spots on the legs that help it to smell and taste.

Each of the daddy-longlegs' eight legs ends with a tiny hook. It uses these to grab onto things as it walks over them.

Although they look alike, spiders and insects are different. Spiders belong to a family of their own. Spiders are called Arachnids (ah-RACK-nids). Scorpions, ticks, and daddy-longlegs are also arachnids.

INSECT

Insects have a body with three parts.

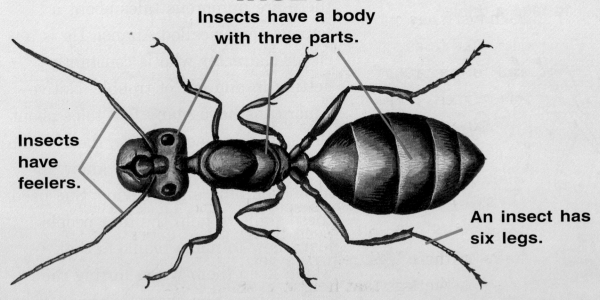

Insects have feelers.

An insect has six legs.

ARACHNID

An arachnid's body has two parts.

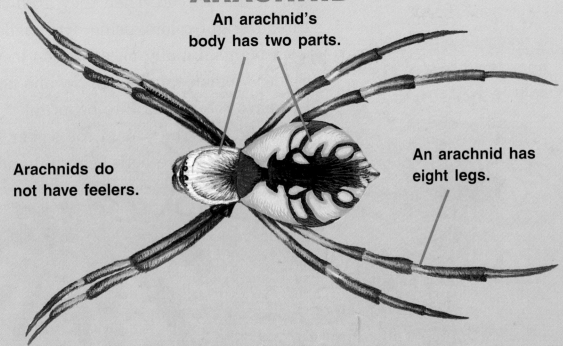

Arachnids do not have feelers.

An arachnid has eight legs.

Did you know a daddy-longlegs can swim? It's so light it can stand on the surface of the water to take a drink.

It takes about one hour for a spider to spin a web.

Spiders in Stories

In many parts of the world, spiders have been featured in stories and folk tales. In Africa and the Caribbean, there are humorous tales about a famous spider called Anansi. He is a clever character who is constantly getting in and out of trouble. Native Americans have many folk tales about the spider. In one of these, the Navaho tell of Spider Woman. She knew all about spinning and weaving. She used these skills to help the first people learn how to make blankets that would keep them warm during the cold winters. She showed them how to take the wool from their sheep and spin it into thread. Then they dyed the thread bright colors, using dyes made from plants. Finally, on a wooden loom, Spider Woman taught the Navaho how to weave the thread into beautiful patterns. Like the web of the spider, these blankets are both beautiful and useful.

The Master Weaver

Round and round, up and down, a hungry spider rushes to weave its web. Later it will rest, waiting for an insect to come by. Nature's web maker knows how to create something beautiful. The web, however, is also useful. It is the key to this spider's survival.

Story Questions & Activities

1. What does a spider use to make a web?

2. Is a tarantula more poisonous than a black widow? Explain.

3. In what ways are spiders helpful to people?

4. What is the main idea of this selection?

5. In "Dream Wolf", a wolf helped two children find their way home. How might a spider have helped the children in that story?

Write a Report

Select a type of spider that you would like to learn more about. Write a report on your spider. Include lots of fun facts and a diagram.

240

Make a Web

Look up pictures of spider webs. Then create your own web. Using a pencil, lightly draw a web on a piece of construction paper. Glue colorful yarn to the lines. Make a spider out of construction paper and paste it to your web.

Interview a Spider

Choose your favorite kind of spider. Write a list of questions that you would like to ask it. With a partner, act out the roles of the spider and a reporter interviewing the spider. Then switch roles.

Find Out More

Black widows are poisonous spiders. What other kinds of spiders are poisonous? Find out more about poisonous spiders. Choose six of them and make a poster. Draw the six spiders, label them, and include facts about each.

STUDY SKILLS

Use a Dictionary

The words in a **dictionary** are arranged alphabetically.
Guide words at the top tell you the first and last word on
the page.

spider A small animal with four pairs of legs, a body divided into two parts, and no wings. Most spiders spin webs to catch insects for food. spi·der (spī′ dər) *noun, plural* **spiders**.

Most spiders spin webs so they can catch insects for food.

spike 1. A, heavy nail used to hold rails to railroad ties. 2. Any sharp, pointed object or part that sticks out: *Baseball shoes have **spikes** on the soles.* spike (spīk) *noun, plural* **spikes**.

spin 1. To turn around quickly: *The car's wheels **spun** in the mud. The child **spun** the top.* 2. To make thin fibers into thread. 3. To make a web or cocoon by giving off a sticky substance that hardens into thread: *Spiders **spin** webs.* 4. To tell: *Our counselor at camp was good at **spinning** ghost stories.* 5. To feel dizzy: *The sun made my head **spin**. Verb.*
spin (spin) *verb*, **spun**, **spinning**; *noun, plural* **spins**.

spindle A stick or rod on or around which something is turned. Fibers of cotton are spun into thread from a spindle. spin·dle (spin′dəl) *noun, plural* **spindles**.

spine 1. The column of bones in the back; backbone. Look up backbone for more information. 2. A sharp, pointed growth on a plant or animal. *The quills of a porcupine are **spines**.* spine (spīn) *noun, plural* **spines**.

spiral A curve that keeps winding. A spiral may wind inward and outward or downward and upward. Some springs are spirals. *Noun.*

• To move in or take the shape of a spiral. *Verb.*

• Having the shape or form of a spiral: *a **spiral** staircase. Adjective.*
spi·ral (spī′rəl) *noun, plural* **spirals**; *verb*, **spiraled**, **spiraling**; *adjective*.

This building is built in the shape of a spiral

PRONUNCIATION KEY

| at | āpe | fär | câre | end | mē | it | ice | pîerce | hot | ōld | sông | fôrk |
| oil | out | up | ūse | rüle | pull | tûrn | chin | sing | shop | thin | this | |

hw in white; zh in treasure. The symbol ə stands for the unstressed vowel sound in about, taken, pencil, lemon, and circus.

Use the dictionary to answer these questions.

1 What are the **guide words** for this dictionary page?

2 What word comes before *spine*?

3 Is the word *spike* an adjective or a noun?

4 Does the *i* in *spindle* sound like the *i* in *ice* or the *i* in *it*? Use the pronunciation to help you decide.

5 Is the word *spindle* an adjective or a noun?

242

Test Tip

As you read, think about what is happening in the story.

DIRECTIONS:

Read the story. Then read each question about the story.

SAMPLE

Homework for Linda

Linda's father picked up her homework assignments from her teacher, Mr. Smith.

Math:
Complete the problems in Chapter 11. They are similar to the ones you did last week.

Spelling:
You spelled all of the words correctly last week! Your spelling work is complete this week.

Reading:
Finish reading *Mystery Island*. The book report will be due next week. Your book reports have been excellent. Keep up the good work!

Geography:
Highlight the capitals on the map of the United States.
Get well soon!
—Mr. Smith and your classmates

1 According to the letter, Linda does NOT have work in —

○ math

○ spelling

○ geography

○ reading

2 From Mr. Smith's note, Linda probably thinks that her teacher is —

○ angry

○ bored

○ caring

○ unkind

Why are your answers correct?

Stories in Art

This coiled basket was made by a Native American woman. She is a member of the Hopi people who live in northeast Arizona.

Look at the basket. What can you tell about it? What is woven into the center of the basket? How is it different from a real spider? How is it the same? What other details do you notice about the basket?

Close your eyes. What do you remember about the basket? Why?

Unusual Hopi Coiled Basket with Spider Design
by Kathryn Kooyahoema

Web
Wonders

A New Spin on Spider Silk

About 800 years ago, a ruler named Genghis Khan went to fight a war. An old story tells how enemy arrows bounced off his soldiers. What was their secret? Spider silk! It was woven into their clothes and their armor.

Today, scientists still have not come up with a thread stronger than the silk spiders use to spin their webs.

Scientists think that a giant spider-silk web could stop a jet plane! And the strands of the web would only have to be as thick as a pencil.

Spiders cannot be raised on farms. (They eat one another.) So scientists are trying to make spider silk without the spiders!

Webs are made from as much as 65 feet of spider silk.

247

JOE MCDONALD/CORBIS

Baby spiders are called "spiderlings." Winds gently carry the spiderlings to new homes.

DID YOU KNOW? AMAZING SPIDER FACTS

◆ Baby spiders hatch from eggs. Then they spin a long silk line. They wait for a breeze to carry them to a new home. The wind has carried some baby spiders 200 miles away.

◆ Spiders spin sticky webs to catch insects. Then they eat them.

◆ The web of a golden silk spider is strong enough to trap a bird.

◆ Spiders have eight legs. Most have eight eyes.

◆ Farmers like to have most spiders around. They eat insects that can hurt farm crops.

248

Scientists have come up with the first few bits of human-made spider silk. They hope to use it in many ways. Try this on for size: One day your favorite jeans may have some spider silk in them. Then they won't wear out so fast. Car bumpers may be made of spider silk so they won't dent so easily. One day, bridges may have spider silk in them so they will not fall down in an earthquake.

So far, none of the human-made silk is as strong as real spider silk. But scientists will continue to work on the problem.

The silk spiders make is a truly amazing fiber. That's one reason scientists have so much respect for spiders.

Tarantulas do not spin webs. They live in holes in the ground.

Two dragonflies are caught in a spider's sticky web. They will be a meal for the spider.

FIND OUT MORE
Visit our website:
www.mhschool.com/reading

*inter***NET**
CONNECTION

Based on an article in *TIME FOR KIDS*.

Story Questions & Activities

1. Why can't spiders be raised on farms?

2. In what ways might a shirt of human-made spider silk be different from a cotton shirt?

3. How do you feel about spiders? How do you think farmers feel about them? Do you feel the same or different? Explain.

4. What is the main idea of this selection?

5. Which kinds of spiders do you think would be helpful to the community garden in "City Green"? Why?

Write an Essay

Choose one kind of spider. Write about what a day in the life of the spider would be like. Tell your story from a spider's point of view. Be sure to include where your spider lives, what it likes to eat, and what makes it unique.

Create a Spider Diagram

Look up different types of spiders. Choose one and draw a diagram of it. Carefully label each part of the spider. Include some facts about your spider and write them under your diagram.

Draw a Spider Comic Strip

Create a comic strip about a baby spider being carried by the wind to a new home. Draw the panels and the characters in pencil. Add speech balloons. Then color in the strip with markers.

Find Out More

Spider babies are called spiderlings. Find out more about what different kinds of baby animals are called. Make a list of animals and the baby name for each animal. Compare your list with your classmates' lists.

Use a Resource

A dictionary is an alphabetical listing of words that tells the meaning, pronunciation, and other information for each word. An encyclopedia is an alphabetical listing of subjects that gives detailed information about each subject.

spider A small animal with four pairs of legs, a body divided into two parts, and no wings. Most spiders spin webs to catch insects for food. **spi•der** (spī′ dər) *noun, plural* **spiders**.

DICTIONARY

Spider (spī′ dər), any of a large group of small invertebrates, or animals without backbones, that usually spin silken webs. Spiders, along with mites, ticks, and scorpions, belong to a group of animals known as arachnids. Although they are often confused with insects, arachnids differ from insects in that they lack antennae and have four pairs of legs instead of three. Another major difference is that the insect's body is divided into a head, a thorax, and an abdomen, while the spider's body consists of only two sections.

ENCYCLOPEDIA

Use the dictionary and encyclopedia entries to answer these questions.

1. Which resource would you use to find out the difference between spiders and insects?

2. Is *spider* a verb or a noun? How do you know?

3. Which resource would you use if you wanted a short description of what a spider is?

4. Which resource would you use if you wanted to look up detailed information about a spider?

5. Suppose you wanted to find out more about spider webs. Which resource would you use and what key words might you look under?

Test Tip

If the questions seem too hard, go back and read the story again.

DIRECTIONS:

Read the story. Then read each question about the story.

SAMPLE

The Amusement Park

Juanita likes animals and wants to learn about them. This flyer tells about the amusement park she is visiting.

WORLD OF SCIENCE WELCOMES YOU!

The Secret World of Submarines— Take a ride on a real submarine in Science Lake! See underwater creatures and plants.

Timberland Wolves—Visit our new exciting Timberland Wolf <u>exhibit</u>. See live wolves in their natural habitat.

The Planetarium—Come see how the night sky looks from the North Pole or the Equator. See how the planets move in space.

---

1 Why would Juanita like the Timberland Wolves attraction best?

○ She thinks contests are fun.

○ She enjoys looking at stars.

○ She likes animals.

○ She wants a new pet.

2 In the flyer, an <u>exhibit</u> is—

○ a display

○ an animal

○ a telescope

○ a submarine

Why are your answers correct?

253

Who Am I?

The trees ask me,
And the sky,
And the sea asks me
      Who am I?

The grass asks me,
And the sand,
And the rocks ask me
      Who I am.

The wind tells me
At nightfall,
And the rain tells me
      Someone small.

    Someone small
    Someone small
      But a piece
          of
          it
          all.

by Felice Holman

Be Creative!

Different Drum

You like to run in sun,
I like to dance in the shade.
I'm marching in my own parade.
You say follow,
But I may not come.
I hear the beat of a different drum.

Some say I'm crazy,
Some say I'm weird.
I'm just marching to the beat I hear.
Sometimes it's hard,
But sometimes it's fun.
I hear the beat of a different drum.

words and music by Joe Scruggs

Stories in Art

Some paintings have more than one story to tell. If you look closely at the details, you can learn more about the picture.

~~~~~~

Look at the painting. What can you tell about it? What is the main color? Now read the title. Look at the painting again. What are some new details that you notice?

~~~~~~

What kind of music do you think the man is playing? Why?

Jaws
by Gil Mayers

MEET
ISAAC MILLMAN

Isaac Millman wanted to write a story that would introduce hearing children to American Sign Language. This is the language that most deaf people use to communicate with one another. To make sure his story was factual, Millman worked with two teachers at a New York City school for the deaf.

Millman says that you can begin to learn American Sign Language by following the position of the hands and fingers and the arrows shown in the diagrams.

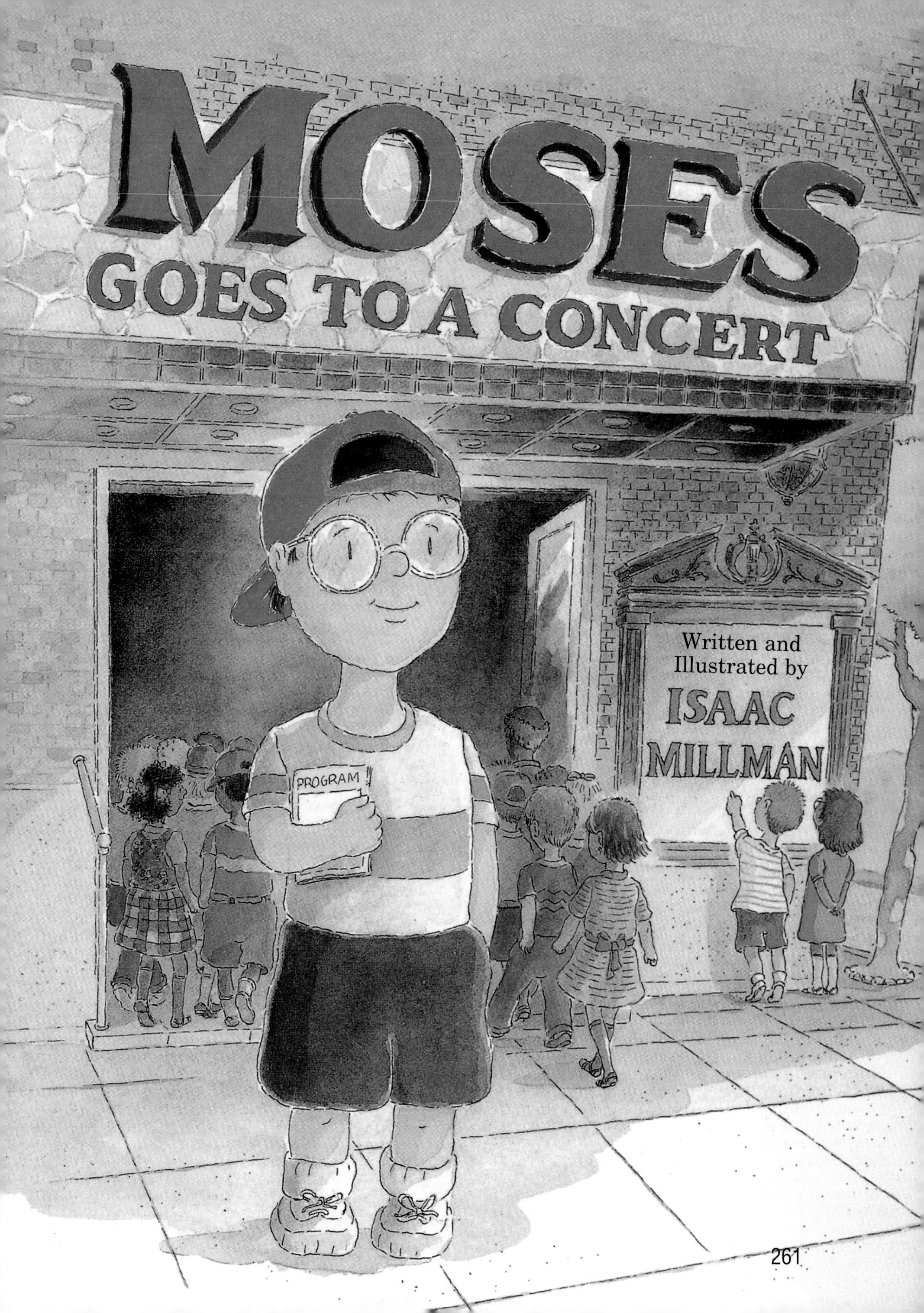
MOSES
GOES TO A CONCERT
PROGRAM
Written and Illustrated by
ISAAC MILLMAN

| I | PLAY | THE DRUM. |

Moses plays on his new drum.

He can't hear the sounds he is making because he is deaf, but he feels the vibration of the drum through his hands. He has taken off his shoes so he can feel it through his feet, too.

HOW TO READ THE ARROWS AND SYMBOLS

Hand moves in directon of arrow

Right arc

Left arc

Swinging movement, back and forth

Repeated movement, forward, back, forward, or up, down, up

Slight wiggling motion

Touching

One motion

Today, Moses is going on a field trip. His teacher, Mr. Samuels, is taking him and his classmates, who are all deaf, to a young people's concert.

As the children climb onto the bus, they wonder what is inside Mr. Samuels's black bag.

"A big surprise," signs Mr. Samuels.

THE TEACHER   HAS   A BIG SURPRISE

On the bus, Moses signs to his friend. "John! My parents gave me a new drum!"

John signs back. "I got one, too!"

MY   FRIEND

Children from all over the city are coming to the
concert. Moses and his friend John wait for their class
to get off the bus so they can go inside together.

Mr. Samuels leads them to their seats in the first row. Across the stage, in front of the orchestra, are all the percussion instruments.

"Children, the percussionist is a friend of mine," signs Mr. Samuels.

"What's a percussionist?" Anna signs back.

"A musician who plays an instrument such as a drum, cymbals, even a piano," replies Mr. Samuels.

A LOUD MUSICAL SOUND

A young woman walks onto the stage. Everyone stands up to applaud. Some of Moses's classmates wave instead of clapping. The percussionist smiles and bows to the audience.

WE · WAVE · AND · APPLAUD.

"She has no shoes!" Moses signs in surprise.

The teacher smiles and signs, "She is deaf, too. She follows the orchestra by feeling the vibrations of the music through her stocking feet."

Then Mr. Samuels takes eleven balloons out of his black bag and hands one to each of his students.

"Oh! What beautiful balloons!" Anna signs.

"Hold them on your laps," signs Mr. Samuels. "They'll help you feel the music."

ELEVEN

BEAUTIFUL

BALLOONS

The conductor turns to face the orchestra and raises his baton.

The percussionist strikes the huge gong and the concert begins.

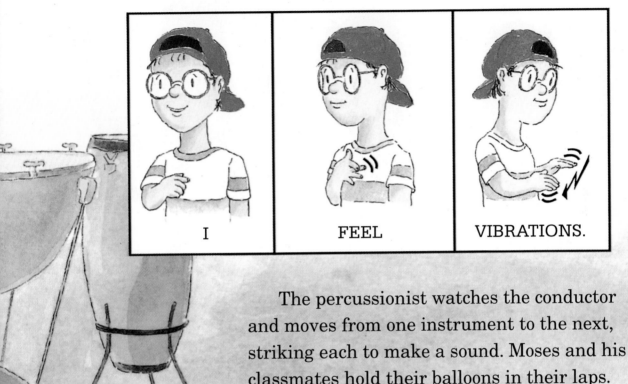

I   FEEL   VIBRATIONS.

The percussionist watches the conductor and moves from one instrument to the next, striking each to make a sound. Moses and his classmates hold their balloons in their laps. They can feel the music as their balloons pick up the vibrations.

When the concert is over, Mr. Samuels has another surprise. He takes the children onstage to meet his friend, Ms. Marjorie Elwyn. "She will tell you how she became a percussionist," signs Mr. Samuels.

"I became seriously ill at the age of seven," signs Ms. Elwyn. "And when I recovered, I found out that I had lost my hearing. I was deaf."

"What did you do then?" signs Moses.

| [MY] FRIENDS | AND | I | ARE DEAF. |

I WORKED HARD.

My HEART WAS SET ON

BECOMING   A PERCUSSIONIST

AND   I   DID.

"Now you can play on my musical instruments," Ms. Elwyn signs. "Come with me, children."

Ann plays on the marimba...
Beverly strikes the triangle...
Mark pounds the floor tom and the cymbal...
Dianne beats the tom-toms...
John hits the snare drum...
and Moses thumps the bass drum...
David strikes the gong...
Tommy and Suzy play on the tubular bells...
while Steve bangs the kettledrum and Maria
plays the congas.

"Children! We have to go!" Mr. Samuels announces after a while. "Ms. Elwyn has to get ready for another concert."

Moses and his classmates sign thank you, and they wave goodbye to Ms. Elwyn.

THANKS   GOODBYE

On the bus on the way home, Moses signs, "It was so much fun!"

SO MUCH

FUN

That night, Moses tells
his parents about the concert.
Here is what he says:

WHEN YOU

SET YOUR MIND TO IT, YOU CAN

BECOME ANYTHING YOU

WANT WHEN YOU GROW UP…

284

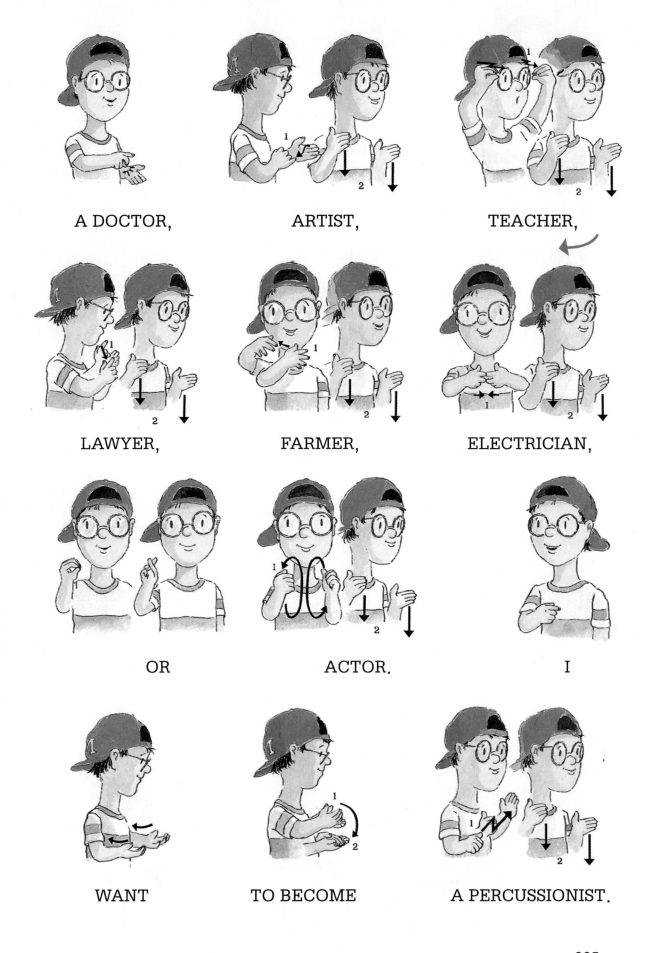

A DOCTOR,   ARTIST,   TEACHER,

LAWYER,   FARMER,   ELECTRICIAN,

OR   ACTOR.   I

WANT   TO BECOME   A PERCUSSIONIST.

1. Why did the children hold balloons at the concert?

2. What did Moses learn from Ms. Elwyn?

3. What made the concert so special for the children?

4. What is this story mainly about?

5. What might the person in the painting on pages 258-259 want to ask Ms. Elwyn?

Write a Letter

Write a letter to the school principal. Try to convince the principal to let your class take a field trip to a concert. Give details about the concert. Tell what the class would learn by going to this concert.

Create a Poster

Music is found in many different cultures all over the world. Choose a country and find out what kinds of instruments are played there. Create a poster that shows some of the instruments and describes them. Include a paragraph about the country, too.

Make a Drum

Find an empty box or coffee can. Cut a piece of wax paper that is big enough to fit over the opening of the box or the can. Cover the opening with the wax paper and pull it tight. Use a rubber band to hold the paper in place. Then play your drum, using two unsharpened pencils as drum sticks.

Find Out More

The character of Ms. Elwyn is based on a real-life musician named Evelyn Glennie. Find out more about her or another musician you find inspiring. If possible, borrow a recording from the library to share with your class.

Use a Diagram

Some hearing-impaired people communicate by using American Sign Language. In this language, words are made with hand shapes, movements, and facial expressions. The **diagram** below shows the hand signs for letters in American Sign Language.

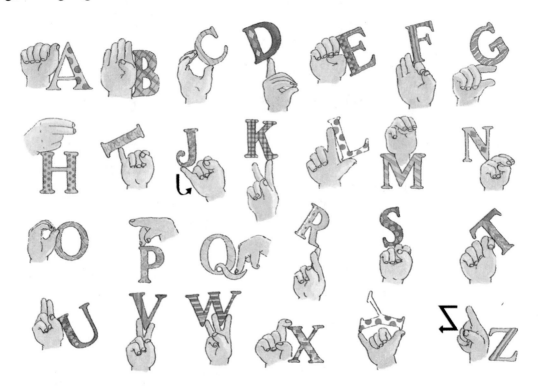

Use the diagram to answer these questions.

1 What is the sign for **I**?

2 How are the signs for **H** and **U** alike?

3 What letter looks the easiest to sign?

4 Sign your name. Was it difficult to do? Why or why not?

5 Why is it good to know something about sign language?

DIRECTIONS:
Read the story. Then read each question about the story.

SAMPLE

A Name for Kitten

Heather picked up her kitten and scratched its ears. She looked at Melissa and said, "I haven't picked a name for her yet. Can you think of one?"

Melissa looked at the kitten's striped fur and said, "I think that her orange fur and the stripes make her look like a tiger. What do you think about that name?" she asked.

Heather smiled. "Tiger is a perfect name!" she said. She had read in an encyclopedia that even the smallest house cat is related to a lion. Her tiny kitten was a cousin of the king of the jungle!

Melissa reached out to pet Tiger. "I love kittens," she said.

"Maybe I'll get one, too."

"Well, you can't have Tiger," Heather said. "She's all mine." The two friends laughed.

1 This story is mostly about—
   ○ lifting up a kitten
   ○ choosing a kitten
   ○ picking a name for a kitten
   ○ two friends laughing

2 Who thought of the name for the kitten?
   ○ Heather's father
   ○ Heather
   ○ Melissa
   ○ The encyclopedia

Stories in Art

Like words on a page, a painting can tell you things. Some things you see right away. Others you have to figure out.

Look at this setting. What can you tell about it? How does the artist show you it is sunny? How do the people feel? Give reasons why you think so.

Close your eyes. What do you remember about the painting? Why?

In Flanders Field by Robert Vonnoh, 1890
Butler Institute of American Art, Youngstown, Ohio

The Little Painter

Meet Patricia Maloney Markun

Patricia Maloney Markun was born and raised in Minnesota. After her marriage, she moved to Panama. She lived there for nineteen years.

In Panama she met Fernando, the boy in *The Little Painter of Sabana Grande*. Markun traveled two days over very rough roads to his tiny village. Seeing Fernando's beautiful paintings, Markun was glad she made the hard trip. Years later, she decided to write a book about him.

Meet Robert Casilla

The Little Painter of Sabana Grande is a favorite of illustrator Robert Casilla. He says, "I related to the story because I too am an artist." Casilla also liked the story because of its Hispanic setting.

Casilla says, "I love doing children's books. There is something magic about them. I like the idea my book will get into a child's hands and communicate a message."

# of Sabana Grande

Written by Patricia Maloney Markun   Illustrated by Robert Casilla

igh in the mountains of Panama lies the village of Sabana Grande. It is very small. Just seven houses of clay adobe stand alongside a brook in a grassy meadow. In the middle house lives the Espino family.

At dawn one cool purple morning, the rooster next door crowed. The Espinos woke up.

Papa went off to the meadow to milk the cow.

Mama stirred up the fire in the open-air kitchen and fried golden breakfast tortillas.

Fernando rolled up his straw sleeping mat and put it in the corner. He hurried to the kitchen to eat his tortilla right away.

This was an important day. At school Fernando had learned to draw colored pictures with crayons. Now school was out for dry-season vacation, and Fernando was going to paint for the first time.

His teacher, Señora Arias, had told him exactly how the country people of Panama made their paints. She said:

"Black from the charcoal of a burned tree stump.
Blue of certain berries that grow deep in the jungle.
Yellow from dried grasses in the meadow.
And red from the clay on the bottom of the brook."

It took him a long time to make the paints. Black was easy, because the burned stump of a big tree lay right next to the Espinos' adobe house.

But Fernando had to look and look before he found those certain berries deep in the jungle, to make the blue paint.

In the corner of the meadow he found a patch of very dry grass, and from that he made a large pot of yellow.

He wandered up and down alongside the brook, looking for clay. The fast-flowing water was too deep for him to reach down to the bottom. At last he came to a bend in the brook where the water was shallow. He reached down and dug up a fistful of clay. It was red, just the way Señora Arias had said.

Now his paints were stirred up and waiting—black, blue, yellow, and red, in four bowls. Next he got out the three paintbrushes his teacher had given him—one very small, one medium-sized, and one especially large.

I'm ready to paint pictures, Fernando said to himself. He picked up the small brush and dipped it into the pot of red. Then he had a terrible thought.

He had nothing to paint a picture on! An artist needs paper.

He looked in both rooms of the house. He could find no paper at all.

He ran from house to house asking everyone in Sabana Grande for paper to paint on. None of the neighbors had any. Not a scrap.

Fernando was sad. After all his work he wouldn't be able to paint pictures—the colored pictures he could almost see, he wanted to make them so badly. Paints and brushes weren't enough. He needed paper, too.

His fingers itched to draw something—anything. He put down the paintbrush and went over to the mud by the brook. He picked up a stick and drew in the wet dirt, the way he had ever since he was a very little boy.

The big rooster who woke him every morning came out of the chicken yard next door. Fernando looked at him and drew the shape of a rooster. He sighed. He couldn't use his new red and yellow paints to make a bright rooster. He couldn't make the rooster's comb red. He could only scratch out a mud-colored rooster. It wasn't the same as painting would be. It didn't have any color.

Fernando looked around at the adobe houses of his village. Suddenly he got an idea. Adobe was smooth and white—almost like paper. Why couldn't he paint on the outside of his family's adobe house?

"No!" Papa said. "Who ever saw pictures on the outside of a house?"

"No!" Mama agreed. "What would the neighbors say?"

Fernando looked at his pots of paint and was very unhappy. He wanted to paint pictures more than anything else he could think of.

At last Papa said, "I can't stand to see my boy so miserable. All right, Fernando. Go ahead and paint on the house!"

Mama said, "Do your best, Fernando. Remember, the neighbors will have to look at your pictures for a very long time."

First Fernando made a tiny plan of the pictures he was going to paint, painting it with his smallest brush on one corner of the house.

"Your plan looks good to me, Fernando," Papa said. "If you can paint pictures small, you should be able to paint them big."

Fernando picked up his bigger brushes and started to paint a huge picture of the most beautiful tree in Panama, the flowering poinciana, on the left side of the front door. As he painted, he could look up and see the red flowers of a poinciana tree, just beginning its dry season, blooming on the mountainside.

The neighbors were very surprised.

Señora Endara called out, "Come and see what Fernando is doing!"

Señor Remon said, "Who ever saw a house with pictures on the outside?"

Pepita, the little girl next door, asked, "Does your mother know you're painting on your house?"

Fernando nodded and smiled and kept on painting. Now and then he would look up at the mountain to see the real poinciana. After a week its flowers faded and died. Fernando's tree grew bigger and brighter and redder.

On one branch he added a black toucan with a flat, yellow bill. On another branch a lazy, brown sloth hung by its three toes.

The neighbors brought out chairs. While Fernando worked, they drank coffee and watched him paint.

Next he painted the wall on the other side of the door. An imaginary vine with flat, green leaves and huge, purple blossoms crept up the wall.

Word spread about the little painter of Sabana Grande. Even people from Santa Marta, the village around the mountain, hiked into town to watch him paint. The purple vine now reached almost to the thatched roof.

One day Señora Arias came from the school in Santa Marta. Why was his teacher looking for him, Fernando wondered. It was still dry season, when there wasn't any school. It hadn't rained for a month.

"School's not starting yet," his teacher said. "I came to see your painted adobe house that everyone in Santa Marta is talking about. Fernando, you did very well with those paintbrushes. I like it!"

She turned to the neighbors. "Don't you?"

"We certainly do!" the neighbors agreed.

They poured some coffee for the visiting teacher.

"Fernando, will you paint pictures on my house?" asked
Señora Alfaro.

"And mine, too?" asked Señor Remon.

Fernando nodded yes, but he kept on painting.

For fun he added a black, white-faced monkey looking down
at the people through purple flowers.

Next to the door he painted a big red-and-yellow rooster,
flopping its red comb as it crowed a loud "cock-a-doodle-doo!"

Above the door he painted the words CASA FAMILIA ESPINO,
so people would know that this was the home of the Espino
family.

Now his pictures were finished. Fernando sat down with his teacher and the neighbors. Everyone said kind words about his paintings.

Fernando said nothing. He just smiled and thought to himself, there are still six adobe houses left to paint in Sabana Grande.

Story Questions & Activities

1. Where does the story take place?

2. How is the setting important to the story?

3. Who do you think gave Fernando the most help? Explain.

4. What is this story mainly about?

5. Imagine that Fernando became part of the painting on pages 290-291. What do you think he would say to the other people in the painting?

Write a Letter

Pretend you are Fernando. Write a letter to a family in Santa Marta to persuade them to let you paint their house. Give three good reasons.

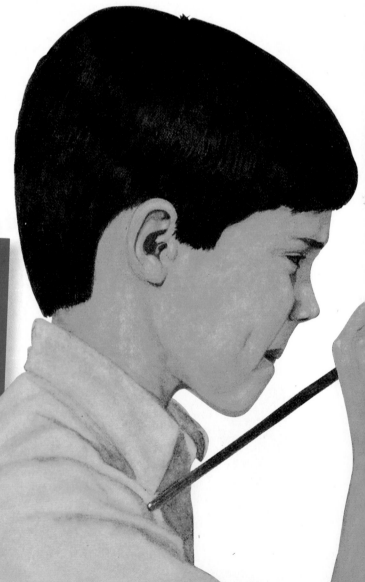

Create a Mural

Fernando painted murals on his house of his village's plants and animals. Plan a mural of some plants and animals from your community. Using a long sheet of paper, create the mural. Give it a title, and sign it in one corner.

What happens when you mix different colors of paint? Create a poster to show what happens. Use some red, blue, and yellow paint. Mix red and blue paint. What color do you get? Try mixing other colors.

Mix Colors of Paint

Find Out More

Fernando's school is closed for the dry season. What months are schools open in Panama? What is a school day like? Start by checking an encyclopedia. Then compare schools there with your school.

Read a Map

The country of Panama lies in Central America. It is home to a great many plants and animals. Sabana Grande is a village in central Panama. Like many other villages in Panama, Sabana Grande is a rural community—a place of farms or open country.

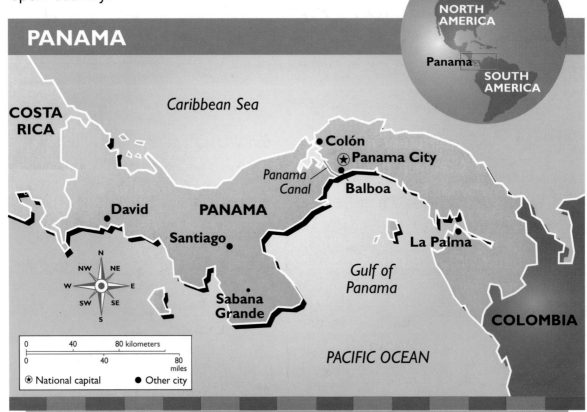

PANAMA

NORTH AMERICA

Panama

SOUTH AMERICA

COSTA RICA

Caribbean Sea

• Colón

⍟ Panama City

Panama Canal

Balboa

David

PANAMA

Santiago

La Palma

Gulf of Panama

N NW NE W E SW SE S

Sabana Grande

COLOMBIA

0   40   80 kilometers
0   40   80 miles

⍟ National capital   • Other city

PACIFIC OCEAN

Use the map to answer these questions.

1 What is the capital of Panama?

2 What country is on the western border of Panama?

3 What are the three cities closest to the Panama Canal?

4 In which direction is Sabana Grande from David?

5 Why do you think Panama has been called the "crossroads of the Americas"?

316

DIRECTIONS:

Read the story. Then read each question about the story.

SAMPLE

October 16

Dear Diary,

Remember when I told you that my friend Ralph has trouble with math? Last night I helped him with some homework problems. Ralph is very smart, but math is his least favorite subject. I showed him how to do long division. It took him a while, but he finally got it. He did all twenty of the practice problems correctly.

Today, Mr. Deevers gave us a surprise math quiz. I looked at Ralph and knew he was nervous.

Mr. Deevers gave us back our tests at the end of class. Ralph got a perfect score and so did I. It made me very happy to have helped out my friend.
—Damon

1 How did Ralph feel when he had to take the surprise quiz?

  ○ Nervous

  ○ Excited

  ○ Bored

  ○ Happy

2 This story is mostly about—

  ○ two friends who have trouble with math

  ○ Mr. Deevers' surprise quiz

  ○ why Damon likes math

  ○ how Damon helped Ralph with math

317

Stories in Art

This quilt is made from pieces of kente cloth. Kente cloth is a famous fabric made by Ashanti weavers in Africa. Now kente cloth is popular all over the world. The woman who made this quilt lives in Georgia.

Look at the quilt. What details do you notice? What can you tell about the person who made it? Why do you think she used kente cloth to make the quilt?

Look at the quilt again. What kinds of shapes do you see? What patterns do you notice?

African-American Kente Cloth Quilt by Ruby Jackson

VALERIE FLOURNOY

Valerie Flournoy was thinking about the members of her own family when she wrote *The Patchwork Quilt*. She was especially remembering her Grandma Buchanan and how much fun they had had together when Valerie was growing up.

Flournoy hopes children who read her story will have respect "not only for their own parents and grandparents but for all of their 'family'—their ancestors—who have gone before them."

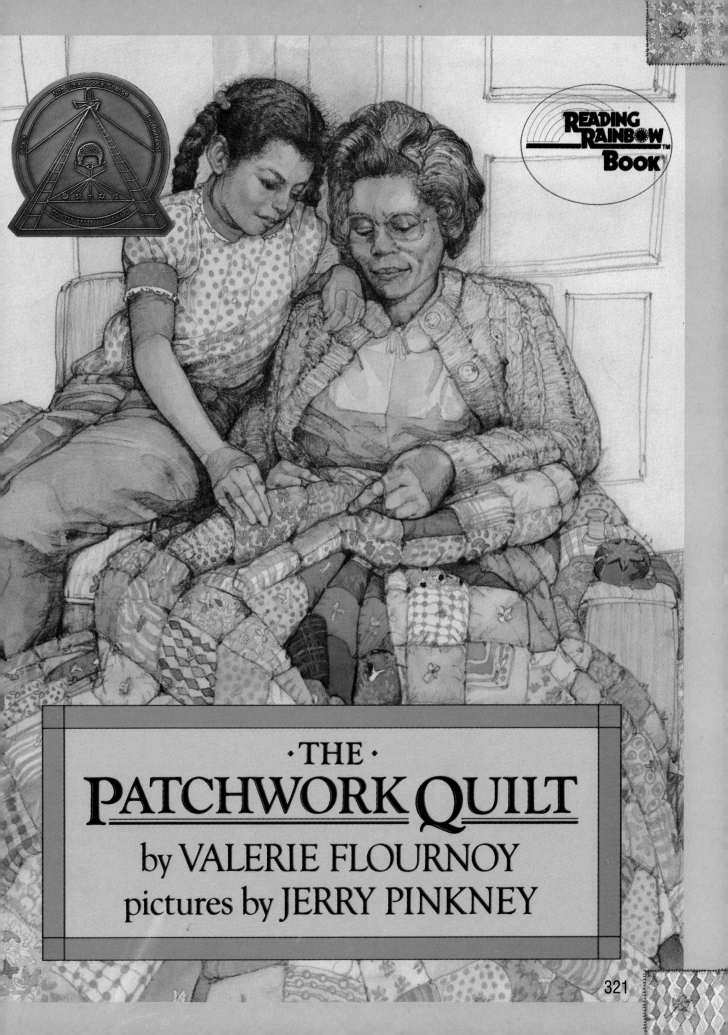

· THE ·
PATCHWORK QUILT

by VALERIE FLOURNOY
pictures by JERRY PINKNEY

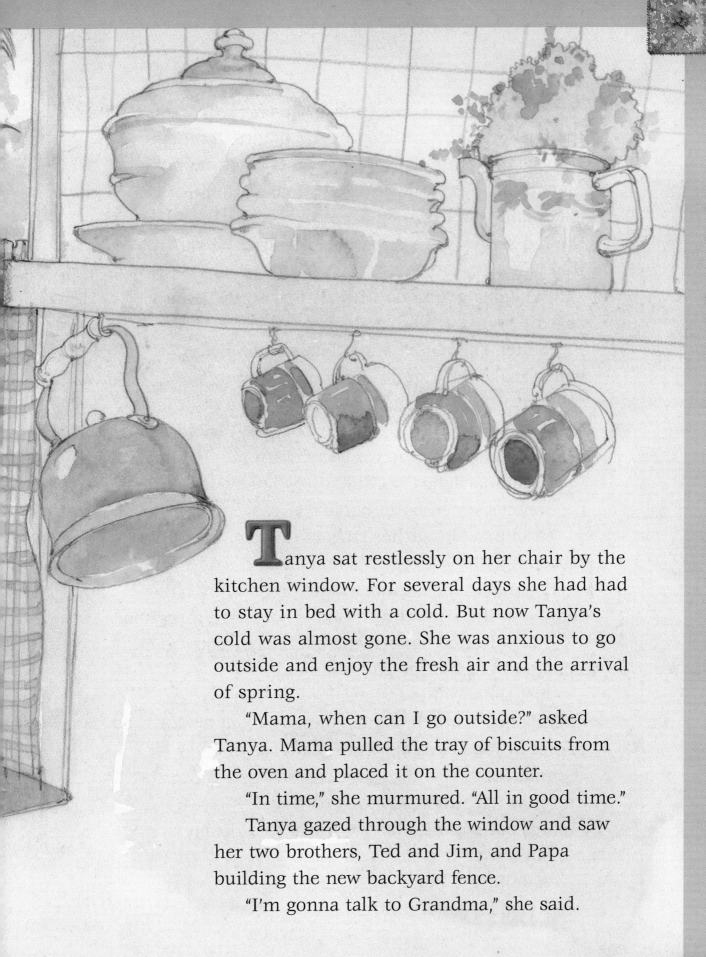

Tanya sat restlessly on her chair by the kitchen window. For several days she had had to stay in bed with a cold. But now Tanya's cold was almost gone. She was anxious to go outside and enjoy the fresh air and the arrival of spring.

"Mama, when can I go outside?" asked Tanya. Mama pulled the tray of biscuits from the oven and placed it on the counter.

"In time," she murmured. "All in good time."

Tanya gazed through the window and saw her two brothers, Ted and Jim, and Papa building the new backyard fence.

"I'm gonna talk to Grandma," she said.

Grandma was sitting in her favorite spot—the big soft chair in front of the picture window. In her lap were scraps of materials of all textures and colors. Tanya recognized some of them. The plaid was from Papa's old work shirt, and the red scraps were from the shirt Ted had torn that winter.

"Whatcha gonna do with all that stuff?" Tanya asked.

"Stuff? These ain't stuff. These little pieces gonna make me a quilt, a patchwork quilt."

Tanya tilted her head. "I know what a quilt is, Grandma. There's one on your bed, but it's old and dirty and Mama can never get it clean."

Grandma sighed. "It ain't dirty, honey. It's worn, the way it's supposed to be."

Grandma flexed her fingers to keep them from stiffening. She sucked in some air and said, "My mother made me a quilt when I wasn't any older than you. But sometimes the old ways are forgotten."

Tanya leaned against the chair and rested her head on her grandmother's shoulder.

Just then Mama walked in with two glasses of milk and some biscuits. Mama looked at the scraps of material that were scattered all over. "Grandma," she said, "I just cleaned this room, and now it's a mess."

"It's not a mess, Mama," Tanya said through a mouthful of biscuit. "It's a quilt."

"A quilt! You don't need these scraps. I can get you a quilt," Mama said.

Grandma looked at her daughter and then turned to her grandchild. "Yes, your mama can g[et] you a quilt from any department store. But it wo[n't] be like my patchwork quilt, and it won't last as long either."

Mama looked at Grandma, then picked up Tanya's empty glass and went to make lunch.

Grandma's eyes grew dark and distant. She turned away from Tanya and gazed out the window, absent-mindedly rubbing the pieces of material through her fingers.

"Grandma, I'll help you make your quilt," Tanya said.

"Thank you, honey."

"Let's start right now. We'll be finished in no time."

Grandma held Tanya close and patted her head. "It's gonna take quite a while to make this quilt, not a couple of days or a week—not even a month. A good quilt, a masterpiece . . ." Grandma's eyes shone at the thought. "Why I need more material. More gold and blue, some red and green. And I'll need the time to do it right. It'll take me a year at least."

"A year," shouted Tanya. "That's too long. I can't wait that long, Grandma."

Grandma laughed. "A year ain't that long, honey. Makin' this quilt gonna be a joy. Now run along and let Grandma rest." Grandma turned her head toward the sunlight and closed her eyes.

"I'm gonna make a masterpiece," she murmured, clutching a scrap of cloth in her hand, just before she fell asleep.

"**W**e'll have to get you a new pair and use these old ones for rags," Mama said as she hung the last piece of wash on the clothesline one August afternoon.

Jim was miserable. His favorite blue corduroy pants had been held together with patches; now they were beyond repair.

"Bring them here," Grandma said.

Grandma took part of the pant leg and cut a few blue squares. Jim gave her a hug and watched her add his patches to the others.

"A quilt won't forget. It can tell your life story," she said.

The arrival of autumn meant school and Halloween. This year Tanya would be an African princess. She danced around in the long, flowing robes Mama had made from several yards of colorful material. The old bracelets and earrings Tanya had found in a trunk in the attic jingled noisily as she moved. Grandma cut some squares out of the leftover scraps and added Tanya to the quilt too!

The days grew colder but Tanya and her brothers didn't mind. They knew snow wasn't far away. Mama dreaded winter's coming. Every year she would plead with Grandma to move away from the drafty window, but Grandma wouldn't budge.

"Grandma, please," Mama scolded. "You can sit here by the heater."

"I'm not your grandmother, I'm your mother," Grandma said. "And I'm gonna sit here in the Lord's light and make my masterpiece."

It was the end of November when Ted, Jim, and Tanya got their wish. They awoke one morning to find everything in sight covered with snow. Tanya got dressed and flew down the stairs. Ted and Jim, and even Mama and Papa, were already outside.

"I don't like leaving Grandma in that house by herself," Mama said. "I know she's lonely."

Tanya pulled herself out of the snow being careful not to ruin her angel. "Grandma isn't lonely," Tanya said happily. "She and the quilt are telling each other stories."

Mama glanced questioningly at Tanya, "Telling each other stories?"

"Yes, Grandma says a quilt never forgets!"

The family spent the morning and most of the afternoon sledding down the hill. Finally, when they were all numb from the cold, they went inside for hot chocolate and sandwiches.

"I think I'll go sit and talk to Grandma," Mama said.

"Then she can explain to you about our quilt— our very own family quilt," Tanya said.

Mama saw the mischievous glint in her youngest child's eyes.

"Why, I may just have her do that, young lady," Mama said as she walked out of the kitchen.

Tanya leaned over the table to see into the living room. Grandma was hunched over, her eyes close to the fabric as she made tiny stitches. Mama sat at the old woman's feet. Tanya couldn't hear what was said but she knew Grandma was telling Mama all about quilts and how *this* quilt would be very special. Tanya sipped her chocolate slowly, then she saw Mama pick up a piece of fabric, rub it with her fingers, and smile.

From that moment on both women spent their winter evenings working on the quilt. Mama did the sewing while Grandma cut the fabrics and placed the scraps in a pattern of colors. Even while they were cooking and baking all their Christmas specialties during the day, at night they still worked on the quilt. Only once did Mama put it aside. She wanted to wear something special Christmas night, so she bought some gold material and made a beautiful dress. Tanya knew without asking that the gold scraps would be in the quilt too.

There was much singing and laughing that Christmas. All Grandma's sons and daughters and nieces and nephews came to pay their respects. The Christmas tree lights shone brightly, filling the room with sparkling colors. Later, when everyone had gone home, Papa said he had never felt so much happiness in the house. And Mama agreed.

When Tanya got downstairs the next morning, she found Papa fixing pancakes.

"Is today a special day too?" asked Jim.

"Where's Mama?" asked Tanya.

"Grandma doesn't feel well this morning," Papa said. "Your mother is with her now till the doctor gets here."

"Will Grandma be all right?" Ted asked.

Papa rubbed his son's head and smiled. "There's nothing for you to worry about. We'll take care of Grandma."

Tanya looked into the living room. There on the back of the big chair rested the patchwork quilt. It was folded neatly, just as Grandma had left it.

"Mother didn't want us to know she wasn't feeling well. She thought it would spoil our Christmas," Mama told them later, her face drawn and tired, her eyes a puffy red. "Now it's up to all of us to be quiet and make her as comfortable as possible." Papa put an arm around Mama's shoulder.

"Can we see Grandma?" Tanya asked.

"No, not tonight," Papa said. "Grandma needs plenty of rest."

It was nearly a week, the day before New Year's, before the children were permitted to see their grandmother. She looked tired and spoke in whispers.

"We miss you, Grandma," Ted said.

"And your muffins and hot chocolate," added Jim. Grandma smiled.

"Your quilt misses you too, Grandma," Tanya said. Grandma's smile faded from her lips. Her eyes grew cloudy.

"My masterpiece," Grandma sighed. "It would have been beautiful. Almost half finished." The old woman closed her eyes and turned away from her grandchildren. Papa whispered it was time to leave. Ted, Jim, and Tanya crept from the room.

Tanya walked slowly to where the quilt lay. She had seen Grandma and Mama work on it. Tanya thought real hard. She knew how to cut the scraps, but she wasn't certain of the rest. Just then Tanya felt a hand resting on her shoulder. She looked up and saw Mama.

"Tomorrow," Mama said.

New Year's Day was the beginning. After the dishes were washed and put away, Tanya and Mama examined the quilt.

"You cut more squares, Tanya, while I stitch some patches together," Mama said.

Tanya snipped and trimmed the scraps of material till her hands hurt from the scissors. Mama watched her carefully, making sure the squares were all the same size. The next day was the same as the last. More snipping and cutting. But Mama couldn't always be around to watch Tanya work. Grandma had to be looked after. So Tanya worked by herself. Then one night, as Papa read them stories, Jim walked over and looked at the quilt. In it he saw patches of blue. His blue. Without saying a word Jim picked up the scissors and some scraps and started to make squares. Ted helped Jim put the squares in piles while Mama showed Tanya how to join them.

Every day, as soon as she got home from school, Tanya worked on the quilt. Ted and Jim were too busy with sports, and Mama was looking after Grandma, so Tanya worked alone. But after a few weeks she stopped. Something was wrong—something was missing, Tanya thought. For days the quilt lay on the back of the chair. No one knew why Tanya had stopped working. Tanya would sit and look at the quilt. Finally she knew. Some*thing* wasn't missing. Some*one* was missing from the quilt.

That evening before she went to bed Tanya tiptoed into Grandma's room, a pair of scissors in her hand. She quietly lifted the end of Grandma's old quilt and carefully removed a few squares.

February and March came and went as Mama proudly watched her daughter work on the last few rows of patches. Tanya always found time for the quilt. Grandma had been watching too. The old woman had been getting stronger and stronger as the months passed. Once she was able, Papa would carry Grandma to her chair by the window. "I needs the Lord's light," Grandma said. Then she would sit and hum softly to herself and watch Tanya work.

"Yes, honey, this quilt is nothin' but a joy," Grandma said.

Summer vacation was almost here. One June day Tanya came home to find Grandma working on the quilt again! She had finished sewing the last few squares together; the stuffing was in place, and she was already pinning on the backing.

"Grandma!" Tanya shouted.

Grandma looked up. "Hush, child. It's almost time to do the quilting on these patches. But first I have some special finishing touches . . ."

The next night Grandma cut the final thread with her teeth. "There. It's done," she said. Mama helped Grandma spread the quilt full length.

Nobody had realized how big it had gotten or how beautiful. Reds, greens, blues, and golds, light shades and dark, blended in and out throughout the quilt.

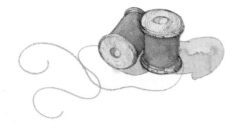

"It's beautiful," Papa said. He touched the gold patch, looked at Mama, and remembered. Jim remembered too. There was his blue and the red from Ted's shirt. There was Tanya's Halloween costume. And there was Grandma. Even though her patch was old, it fit right in.

343

They all remembered the past year. They especially remembered Tanya and all her work. So it had been decided. In the right hand corner of the last row of patches was delicately stitched, "For Tanya from your Mama and Grandma."

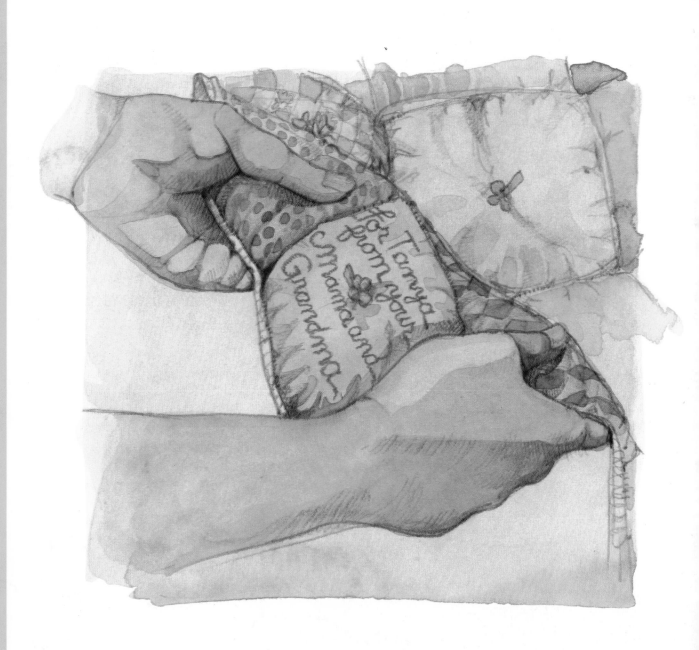

JERRY PINKNEY

Jerry Pinkney's elementary school teachers often asked him to draw on the chalkboard for class projects. The artist says that this made him feel special, because he has loved to draw for as long as he can remember.

Today Jerry Pinkney spends much of his time in libraries. He looks for information to add just the right details to his illustrations. You can see some of these details in *The Patchwork Quilt,* which won the Coretta Scott King Award for Illustration. Among the many other books the artist has illustrated are *Rabbit Makes a Monkey of Lion* and *Turtle in July.*

Story Questions & Activities

1. Where did Grandma get the cloth for the squares on her quilt?

2. What do you think Grandma meant when she said, "Sometimes the old ways are forgotten"?

3. Do you think Tanya will make another quilt some day? Why or why not?

4. What is this story mostly about?

5. Pretend Tanya and Fernando Espino are working together on a quilt. What do you think the quilt would look like?

Write an Editorial

Write an editorial for your school paper. Explain why it is important for young people and older people to work together. Tell what they might learn from each other. Support your ideas with examples.

Design a Geometric Quilt

With a pencil, divide a piece of paper into four equal rectangles or triangles. Using only triangles and rectangles, create a different design for each of the four sections. Use markers to color in your designs.

Create a Scrapbook

Make a scrapbook to record special memories. Take several sheets of paper. Cut two pieces of poster board the same size as your paper. Use the poster board to form the cover of your book. Staple the cover and pages in place. Decorate the cover with colored markers.

Find Out More

Making quilts is a tradition in many cultures. Look for pictures of different kinds of quilts. Bring in the pictures for a class display. How are the quilts alike? How are they different?

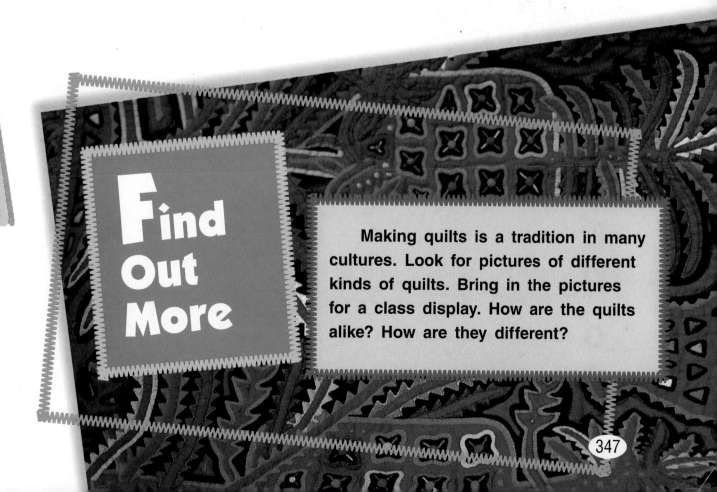

Use a Diagram

A diagram is a picture that shows the parts of something. The diagram below shows a pattern for making a quilt. You will need paper, scissors, glue, crayons, and construction paper to make a paper quilt.

A1	A2	A3
B1	B2	B3
C1	C2	C3

Follow directions 1–4. Then answer question 5.

1 Trace the diagram onto a sheet of paper. Color each square a different color, but don't cover up the numbers and letters.

2 Cut out the squares.

3 Arrange the squares in order on a piece of construction paper.

4 Glue each square onto the construction paper.

5 What colors are in Row 2? Row 3?

DIRECTIONS:
Read the story. Then read each question about the story.

SAMPLE

Randy and the Beaver

One day, Randy the park ranger was walking near the pond. He saw a baby beaver chewing on a log. Winter was coming soon and so Randy decided that he would make a house for the little beaver.

He went home and came back with some old wood, nails, and a hammer. When Randy was finished building the house, he hid behind a tree to see if the beaver would use the house.

Soon the beaver came up to the house. But instead of going inside, he started to chew on the wood.

Randy chuckled and said, "Next time, I'll know better. You're the best one to build a house for yourself. You can only be what you are—a beaver."

1 How did Randy feel about the beaver at the end of the story?

○ Happy

○ Upset

○ Worried

○ Angry

2 The main idea of this story is that Randy—

○ learned that animals will be themselves

○ should make another house for the beaver

○ has too many pets

○ will need to get more nails

Stories in Art

Cold Morning on the Range
by Frederic Remington, 1904
Gerald Peters Gallery, Santa Fe, New Mexico

The artist painted this picture almost 100 years ago. It shows what life was like for the people who lived out West.

Look at the painting. What can you tell about the setting? What do you think the man on the horse is doing? What can you tell about him? What do you think will happen next?

Close your eyes. What details do you remember about the painting?

Meet Angela Shelf Medearis

"As a child I loved to pretend I was the heroine in fairy tales," says Angela Shelf Medearis. "I've always loved to read but I can't recall ever reading any books by or about African Americans when I was in elementary school."

When Medearis grew up she changed all that. She became a children's book author and has made a difference with her writing. Funny and award-winning books like *Zebra Riding Cowboy*, *Dancing with the Indians*, and *Poppa's New Pants* have helped make Medearis one of Texas's most popular children's authors.

"I really, really like to make kids laugh," she says. "It's one of the happiest sounds in the world."

Meet John Kanzler

John Kanzler lives in Connecticut with his wife Diane, also an artist, in a small house surrounded by woods. Animals and insects are his favorite things to draw, and he can often see deer, turkey, and coyotes, running or napping in his yard. He says, "Although I have never ridden a horse in my life, I wanted painting Pecos Bill to feel like the closest thing to going out West and wrangling mustangs myself!"

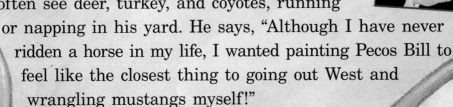

PECOS BILL

"A Tall Tale Play"

by Playwright Angela Shelf Medearis
Illustrated by John Kanzler

Narrative Characters

COOKIE, THE COOK

NARRATOR/COWGIRL PAM

NARRATOR/COWBOY SAM

RANCH HAND 1

RANCH HAND 2

RANCH HAND 3

Tall Tale Characters

PA

MA

PECOS BILL

OTHER CHILDREN

COYOTES

CARL THE COWBOY

SLUE-FOOT SUE

JUDGE

PRODUCTION NOTE: *In this play the campfire and the benches should be placed stage left. The Narrative Characters will stay in this area during the whole play. Cowboy Sam and Cowgirl Pam will narrate the story. The action of the Tall Tale Characters will take place center stage and stage right.*

SETTING: *A cowboy camp located somewhere in the Southwest. Some benches are pulled up around a campfire.*

COOKIE (*Enters while beating on a pan with a spoon*): Come and get it!

COWBOY SAM: What a day! I'm so hungry I could eat my boots.

RANCH HAND 1: What's for dinner, Cookie?

COOKIE: Beans.

RANCH HAND 2: Did you fix a salad?

COOKIE: I sure did. It's three-bean salad.

RANCH HAND 3: What's for dessert?

COOKIE: Bean pie.

COWGIRL PAM: Cookie, we're tired of eating beans!

RANCH HAND 1: We've had beans for sixty-seven days!

EVERYONE: All you ever cook is beans, beans, beans!

COWGIRL PAM: Don't you know how to cook anything else?

COOKIE: Nope! I only cook what I like to eat and I like beans.

COWBOY SAM: Well, I'm going to order some pizzas.

RANCH HANDS *(together)*: Yeah! Pizza!

COOKIE: Okay! Okay! If you don't want to eat these beans tonight, that's fine. I will just serve them for breakfast in the morning.

(Everyone groans. Cowboy Sam takes a cell phone out from under his cowboy hat and dials some numbers.)

COWGIRL PAM: So, that's why cowboys wear those ten-gallon hats!

COWBOY SAM *(into phone)*: Hello, four large cheese pizzas, please. Oh, you need our address? We're at 555 Middle of Nowhere Road. Okay, see you in thirty minutes.

RANCH HAND 1: Cowgirl Pam, will you tell us a story while we're waiting for our pizzas?

RANCH HAND 2: I want to hear a story about Pecos Bill.

RANCH HAND 3: I want to hear a story about Slue-Foot Sue.

COWGIRL PAM: I'll be glad to tell you all about Pecos Bill and Slue-Foot Sue. Will you help me, Cowboy Sam?

COWBOY SAM: Of course. Listen up, cowpokes! The legend of Pecos Bill and Slue-Foot started right here in the great state of Texas. Now, Bill's Pa couldn't stand to live around too many people.

COWGIRL PAM: It's a good thing that Texas is a big state. Bill's Pa didn't have to move very far when he wanted to be alone.

PA *(runs on stage)*: Ma, we've got new neighbors! It's time to move!

MA *(entering stage followed by some children)*: Where do they live, Pa?

PA: They live over the mountains and through the woods. They're only 150 miles away!

MA: 150 miles! Why, they're almost right in our backyard!

PA: Come on, Ma! Pack up all of the kids! *(exiting with Ma and the children)* Let's go west!

COWGIRL PAM: So, Pa, Ma, Bill, and his fourteen brothers and sisters moved west. They were crossing the Pecos River when their wagon wheel hit a rock. Poor little Bill flew out of the wagon. He hit the ground and stumbled around like a tumbleweed in a Texas tornado.

(Pecos Bill stumbles across stage. He sits down in the center of the stage. He looks around, rubbing his head and looking puzzled.)

COWBOY SAM: Pa and Ma didn't hear a thing.

RANCH HAND 1: Didn't Ma and Pa notice that Pecos Bill was missing?

COWGIRL PAM: Well, Ma tried to count her children every day. But they kept moving around. Sometimes she even counted some of them twice.

MA *(counting children)*: One, two, five, eight, nine…or was that six?

COWBOY SAM: Poor little Bill was left out in the middle of nowhere all by himself.

RANCH HAND 1 *(crying)*: Poor little Bill!

RANCH HAND 2 *(crying)*: All alone in the Texas wilderness!

RANCH HAND 3 *(crying):* When are those pizzas coming? *(everyone looks at Ranch Hand 3)*

RANCH HAND 3: Well, I'm hungry! Go on with the story, Cowboy Sam.

COWBOY SAM: There was a pack of friendly coyotes nearby. They were eating dinner. The coyotes looked at Bill. Bill looked at the coyotes. Pretty soon they came over to see what kind of animal Bill was.

(A mother coyote and her coyote children—about four to six children—run over to Bill.)

COYOTES *(together)*: AHOOOOO!

PECOS BILL: Goo-goo.

COWBOY SAM: Now, it turns out that goo-goo means "I'm lost, hungry, and feeling very alone, please help me right now!" in coyote language.

COWGIRL PAM: The kind mother coyote took Bill to her den. Then she gave him a nice, juicy piece of meat.

(Bill sniffs the meat and gobbles it down.)

COYOTES: AHOOOOO!

PECOS BILL: Goo-goo.

COWBOY SAM: From that day on, Bill joined the coyote family. He ran and played with them during the day. And he sang with them on moonlit nights.

(The coyotes and Bill howl at the moon.)

COWGIRL PAM: Bill was a very happy coyote.

COWBOY SAM: Years later, a cowboy named Carl saw Pecos Bill. Carl the Cowboy changed Pecos Bill's life forever.

(Carl the Cowboy gallops on stage. Bill and the coyotes are playing and eating.)

CARL THE COWBOY: Whoa! Why, that coyote looks almost human! Wait a minute. That coyote *is* a human. It's a boy!

(Carl the Cowboy grabs Bill by the leg. Bill tries to run away. The coyotes run offstage.)

CARL THE COWBOY: I'm Carl the Cowboy. What's your name?

PECOS BILL: AHOOOO! AHOOO! AH, AH, AH, BILLLLLLLLL!

CARL THE COWBOY: Did you say your name is Bill?

PECOS BILL: I, I—*(coughs loudly)* Yes! Yes! My name is Bill!

CARL THE COWBOY: Why in the world are you crawling around in the dirt like a coyote?

PECOS BILL: Because I am a coyote.

CARL THE COWBOY: Son, you are not a coyote.

PECOS BILL: Yes, I am. I can run faster than a lizard. I can jump higher than a jack rabbit. And I can howl louder than the wind.

CARL THE COWBOY: I can do all that stuff, too. Son, you need a good, hot bath. Come along with me. I'm going to teach you how to be a cowboy.

COWGIRL PAM: For three long days, Carl the Cowboy taught Pecos Bill how to think, walk, talk, and ride like a cowboy. He gave him a book called *How to Be a Cowboy in Ten Easy Lessons.*

(Carl shows him how cowboys walk. They skip around on the stage. He mimes how to ride a horse.)

CARL THE COWBOY: Well, I've taught you everything I know. I've got to go now. I'm on my way to see my Pa and help him with his ranch.

PECOS BILL: My Pa was named Pa, too.

CARL THE COWBOY: Was your Ma named Ma?

PECOS BILL: Yes!

CARL THE COWBOY: Do you have fourteen brothers and sisters?

PECOS BILL: I sure do!

CARL THE COWBOY *(rapidly)*: Do you have a red-haired, freckled-faced brother named Clyde?

PECOS BILL *(sadly)*: No. No, I don't have a red-haired, freckled-faced brother named Clyde.

CARL THE COWBOY *(happily)*: Neither do I! But I do have a brother named Bill. He fell out of a wagon while we were crossing the Pecos River. We always called him Pecos Bill.

PECOS BILL: I fell out of a wagon seventeen years ago. Carl, you must be my brother!

CARL THE COWBOY: And you must be Pecos Bill!

(They embrace and dance around the stage.)

PECOS BILL: I always knew I was different from my coyote family.

CARL THE COWBOY: What made you think you were different?

PECOS BILL: Well, all the other coyotes had tails.

CARL THE COWBOY: Come on! I can't wait for Ma and Pa to see you. They are going to be so surprised. Let's go!

COWBOY SAM: So that's how Carl the Cowboy found his brother Pecos Bill. Pecos Bill said thank you and good-bye to his coyote family.

(Pecos Bill and the coyotes howl and cry together. Then Pecos Bill waves good-bye.)

COWGIRL PAM: Quicker than greased lightning, the two brothers set off across the prairie to see their family. They hadn't gone very far when they saw a beautiful golden mustang.

PECOS BILL: Stand back, Carl! I can handle him.

COWBOY SAM: Pecos Bill ran as fast as a jack rabbit. He chased that horse across several states. Finally he got close enough to grab the mustang by its mane. Pecos Bill swung himself on the horse's back. The horse stopped so quick it plowed up miles and miles of earth. Pecos Bill and the mustang found themselves at the bottom of a deep canyon. Some folks call it the Grand Canyon.

CARL THE COWBOY: Well, if that don't beat all. I think you just invented something new. I've never seen anybody tame a wild horse like that.

PECOS BILL: Let's call it bronco-busting! We can teach it to all the cowboys.

CARL THE COWBOY: That's a great idea. I can't wait for Pa and Ma to see you riding on that wildcat.

PECOS BILL: I'm going to name this horse Widow Maker. Yee-haw!

COWGIRL PAM: Well, Pecos Bill and Carl the Cowboy hadn't gone very far when a big old rattlesnake appeared. Pecos Bill jumped off his horse, grabbed the snake, and held it tight. Next he whirled it around and around his head. That snake got so dizzy it forgot how to bite. Then Pecos Bill used the rattler to rope all the longhorns he saw on the prairie.

CARL THE COWBOY: Well, if that don't beat all. I think you just invented something else! I've never seen anybody round up longhorns like that.

PECOS BILL: Let's call it a lasso! We can teach it to all the cowboys.

RANCH HAND 1: So that's how a lasso was invented.

RANCH HAND 2: And bronco-busting!

RANCH HAND 3: Where is that pizza? *(Everyone looks at Ranch Hand 3.)* Well, I'm hungry! Go on with the story, Cowboy Sam.

COWBOY SAM: Guess what else Pecos Bill invented.

COOKIE: The lima bean?

COWBOY SAM: No! He invented the guitar and cowboy songs.

RANCH HAND 1: How did he do that?

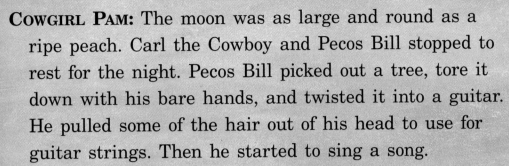

COWGIRL PAM: The moon was as large and round as a ripe peach. Carl the Cowboy and Pecos Bill stopped to rest for the night. Pecos Bill picked out a tree, tore it down with his bare hands, and twisted it into a guitar. He pulled some of the hair out of his head to use for guitar strings. Then he started to sing a song.

PECOS BILL: This is a song the coyotes taught me, Carl. Just listen and sing along with me.

(*Pecos Bill and Carl the Cowboy sing* Home on the Range. *Everyone sings along.*)

RANCH HAND 1: What a beautiful song.

RANCH HAND 2: Now we know how the first guitar was made.

RANCH HAND 3: The pizza is here! Yes!

(*Everyone gets a slice of pizza.*)

RANCH HAND 2: Go on with the story, Cowgirl Pam.

COWGIRL PAM: Do you know how Pecos Bill met his wife, Slue-Foot Sue?

RANCH HAND 1: Tell us!

COWBOY SAM: One day, Pecos Bill and Carl the Cowboy decided to go for a swim in the Rio Grande River. While they were swimming, Pecos Bill saw something strange coming towards them.

SLUE-FOOT SUE: Out of my way you two! Yee-haw!

PECOS BILL: What was that? It looked like a catfish, but it's as big as a whale! And who is that riding that fish like a bronco?

CARL THE COWBOY: That's Slue-Foot Sue!

SLUE-FOOT SUE: Howdy, Carl! Howdy, stranger!

CARL: Howdy, Slue-Foot Sue. Sue, this is my brother, Pecos Bill.

SLUE-FOOT SUE: Howdy, Pecos Bill! I've heard a lot about you.

COWGIRL PAM: Pecos Bill took one look into Slue-Foot Sue's beautiful brown eyes and fell in love. He forgot he was a cowboy and started acting like a coyote again.

PECOS BILL: AHOOOO! AHOOOOOOO! I sure like the way you ride a catfish. Will you marry me?

SLUE-FOOT SUE: Of course I will marry you! Just give me a few minutes to change my clothes.

RANCH HAND 1: That's so sweet.

RANCH HAND 2: That's so romantic.

RANCH HAND 3: That was great pizza.

(Everyone looks at Ranch Hand 3.)

RANCH HAND 3: Well, I was hungry. Go on with the story, Cowgirl Pam.

COWGIRL PAM: Slue-Foot Sue put on a dress she had been saving for a special day. It had 200 yards of shiny satin and a bow as wide as the front porch of a house.

COWBOY SAM: Pecos Bill's whole family came to the wedding. The coyotes sang the wedding march.

(Coyotes sing.)

SLUE-FOOT SUE: I do!

JUDGE: I now pronounce you Cowboy and Cowgirl!

PECOS BILL: AHOOOOOOO!

SLUE-FOOT SUE: He sure has a pretty way with words.

COWGIRL PAM: And they lived happily ever after.

RANCH HAND 1: That was a great tall tale.

RANCH HAND 2: That was fun.

RANCH HAND 3: That was great pizza.

COOKIE: It sure was. I think I'll make pizza from now on. I know! I'll combine beans with pizza!

(Everyone looks at Cookie. They all get up and leave.)

COOKIE *(follows after them)*: How does Lima Bean Pizza sound for breakfast?

The End

Story Questions & Activities

1. Who is telling the story of Pecos Bill?

2. What did Pecos Bill learn from the coyotes?

3. Do you think Pecos Bill was brave? Explain.

4. What is this story mostly about?

5. Pretend that Cowgirl Pam meets Phoebe. What might they talk about? What kinds of stories might they tell each other?

Write a Play Review

Your class is about to put on a performance of "Pecos Bill." Write a review that will convince people to come and see the play. Describe your favorite part of the play.

372

Make a Fact Card

Pecos Bill met Slue-Foot Sue on the Rio Grande. Make a fact card about the Rio Grande. How many miles is it? What states does it flow through? What kind of boats travel the Rio Grande?

Illustrate an Invention

Pecos Bill claims to be the inventor of many things. Can you think of something to invent? How about a new idea for a lunch box? An umbrella? Make an illustration of your invention. Write a caption that tells what your invention does.

Find Out More

What do you know about modern cowboys? Where do they live? What is a typical day like for a cowboy? Find a library book about cowboys and compare Pecos Bill's life with the way cowboys live today.

STUDY SKILLS

Use a Map

A **map** is a drawing that shows information about a place. You might use a map if you were going to visit a new place.

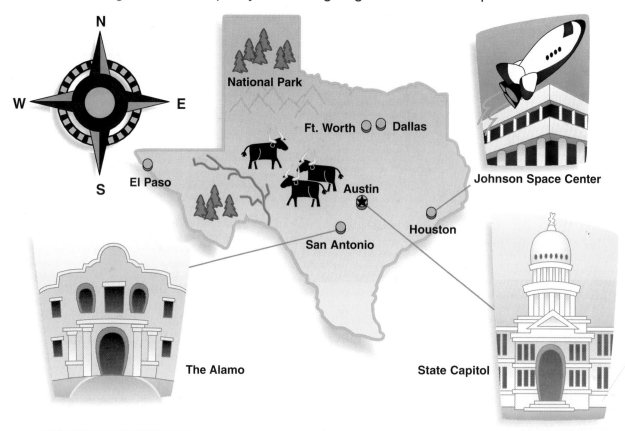

National Park
Ft. Worth ○ ○ Dallas
El Paso
Austin
Johnson Space Center
San Antonio
Houston
The Alamo
State Capitol

Use the map of Texas to answer these questions.

1 What is the state capital of Texas?

2 In which city is the Alamo located?

3 If you went from Houston to El Paso, which direction would you travel?

4 If you wanted to visit the Johnson Space Center, which city would you go to?

5 Which places would you like to visit in Texas? Give reasons for your answers.

Test Tip
Look for clues around the
underlined word to figure
out what it means.

DIRECTIONS:

Read the story. Then read each
question about the story.

SAMPLE

All About the World

There was a little girl who loved to skip and sing. One day another child told the girl that she should not skip and sing at the same time. "If you sing and skip at the same time, you might miss the edge of the world and fall off!" he said.

The girl had never heard that the world had an edge nor that you could fall off. For the rest of the day she was careful not to sing and skip at the same time.

That night, she asked her mother if she could fall off the world if she skipped and sang at the same time.

Her mother smiled and said, "No, no, dear, the world is a sphere. It is round like a big ball and has no edges. Skip and sing as much as you like!"

1 When the child told the girl that the world had edges, she felt—

○ happy

○ worried

○ excited

○ pleased

2 In this story, the word <u>sphere</u> means—

○ shaped like a ball

○ shaped like a square

○ bouncy

○ blue and green

375

Stories in Art

Some artists cut shapes and figures out of different kinds of materials. These forms are called sculptures. The artist who made this sculpture carved it from ice.

Look at the sculpture. What can you tell about it? What details do you notice about the carriage and the animal inside? What will happen to the ice when the weather gets warmer?

Pretend that you are going to carve an ice sculpture. What would you make? Why?

Ice Sculpture at Winterlude, Ottawa, Ontario

TIME
FOR KIDS

SPECIAL REPORT

A VERY COOL PLACE TO VISIT

A hotel in Sweden
is made of ice and snow.

Chill Out!

Sometimes on a winter night, the cold creeps in. It creeps under wool blankets. It creeps into the warmest pajamas. It creeps inside the heaviest socks. *Brrr!* It finds a set of toes to nip.

At one hotel in Sweden, the cold doesn't have to sneak in. Guests *know* it will nip at their toes, fingers, and noses. Welcome to the Ice Hotel! The building and some of the furniture are made of ice and snow.

Why would anyone spend money to stay in a hotel like this? Kerstin Nilsson, who works there, says people love the beauty of the place. "It is pure winter—white and fresh snow." And she says there are "beautiful northern lights in the sky." It is also very quiet.

Guests sleep on beds made of ice and covered with reindeer skins.

A reindeer greets visitors as they arrive at the hotel.

379

This isn't an ice hotel. It's an ice palace! It was built for a winter carnival in Harbin, China.

Each guest gets an extra-warm snowsuit and a sleeping bag for the night. Guests need all the warm things they can get. The hotel's 100 beds are made from ice blocks covered with reindeer skins.

You have to warm yourself up before you get into bed. "Do some push-ups at bedtime," says Johan Woutilainen, a hotel worker. Once inside their sleeping bags, guests stay warm through the night.

FIND OUT MORE

Visit our website:
www.mhschool.com/reading

When visitors leave in the morning, they get a special card. It proves they have conquered the cold by staying at the hotel.

Each spring, when the weather warms up, the hotel melts. When winter comes, a new hotel is built from fresh ice and snow. Once again, the Ice Hotel is ready to welcome people into the cold.

NICE ICE EXPERIMENT

Here is a cold experiment you can do even in the middle of summer!

What You Need

❄ table salt
❄ an ice cube
❄ a piece of string

1.

What You Do

1. Place one end of the string on the ice cube.
2. Sprinkle some salt over the string and the cube.
3. Wait a few seconds. Gently lift the string. The cube will come up with it.

2.

3.

Why It Works

Salt warms the ice and makes it melt. When the salt melts away, the ice freezes again.

ILLUSTRATION FOR TIME FOR KIDS BY BOB STAAKE

Based on an article in *TIME FOR KIDS*.

Story Questions & Activities

1. How do people stay warm when they sleep on beds made of ice?

2. How do you think people might warm up before going to bed?

3. Why do you think visitors get a special card when they leave in the morning? Explain.

4. What is the main idea of this selection?

5. How is the Ice Hotel different from Fernando's house in "The Little Painter of Sabana Grande"? How is it the same?

Write a Letter

Write a letter to your family to persuade them to visit the Ice Hotel for a family vacation. Give reasons why it would be a fun place to visit.

Design a Sugar Hotel

Make a plan to construct a hotel out of sugar cubes. Then use sugar cubes and glue to build the palace. Compare your plan to the finished hotel. Did you make any changes? Display your plan and the hotel in your classroom.

Make a Poster

At what temperature does water freeze and turn into ice? Make a poster showing water turning into ice. Include a thermometer in your drawing showing the temperature at which water freezes. Write some fun facts about ice on your poster.

Find Out More

At the Ice Hotel, guests are greeted by a reindeer. Find out more about reindeer. What kinds of things do they eat? Where do they live? Make a reindeer fact card and illustrate it.

STUDY SKILLS

Use a Map

Maps are used to locate places such as countries or cities. They can also show geographical features such as elevation or climate.

Sweden

EUROPE

CLIMATE OF SWEDEN

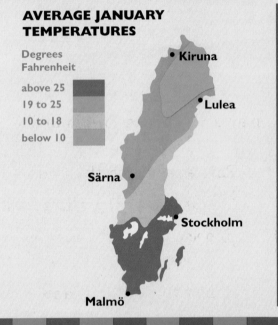

AVERAGE JANUARY TEMPERATURES

Degrees Fahrenheit

above 25
19 to 25
10 to 18
below 10

Kiruna
Lulea
Särna
Stockholm
Malmö

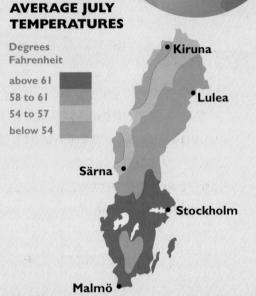

AVERAGE JULY TEMPERATURES

Degrees Fahrenheit

above 61
58 to 61
54 to 57
below 54

Kiruna
Lulea
Särna
Stockholm
Malmö

Use the climate map to answer these questions.

1 What kind of information does a climate map give you?

2 If you wanted to visit Stockholm when the temperature was above 61°F, what month would you go?

3 Why do you think the map gives the temperatures for January and July?

4 Which cities have an average January temperature below 25°F?

5 Which cities have an average July temperature above 57°F?

TEST POWER

Test Tip

If you do not understand a question, read it and the answer choices again.

DIRECTIONS:

Read the story. Then read each question about the story.

SAMPLE

An Instrument for Vincent

Vincent had always liked the guitar and he wanted to learn how to play one. His mother was excited that he wanted to learn how to play a musical instrument. She <u>enrolled</u> Vincent in guitar lessons the next day.

A guitar, Vincent learned, has six strings. The strings go from one end of the instrument to the other. The long part of the guitar is called the neck. Vincent could press the strings on the neck to make different sounds. Vincent learned many ways to use his fingers to make different notes.

Vincent practiced a little every day. Soon he was able to play a short song for his mother.

1 This story is mostly about—

○ learning to play the guitar

○ deciding what instrument to play

○ how to play the piano

○ Vincent's mother taking lessons

2 In this story, <u>enrolled</u> means—

○ signed up

○ gave

○ sang

○ walked around

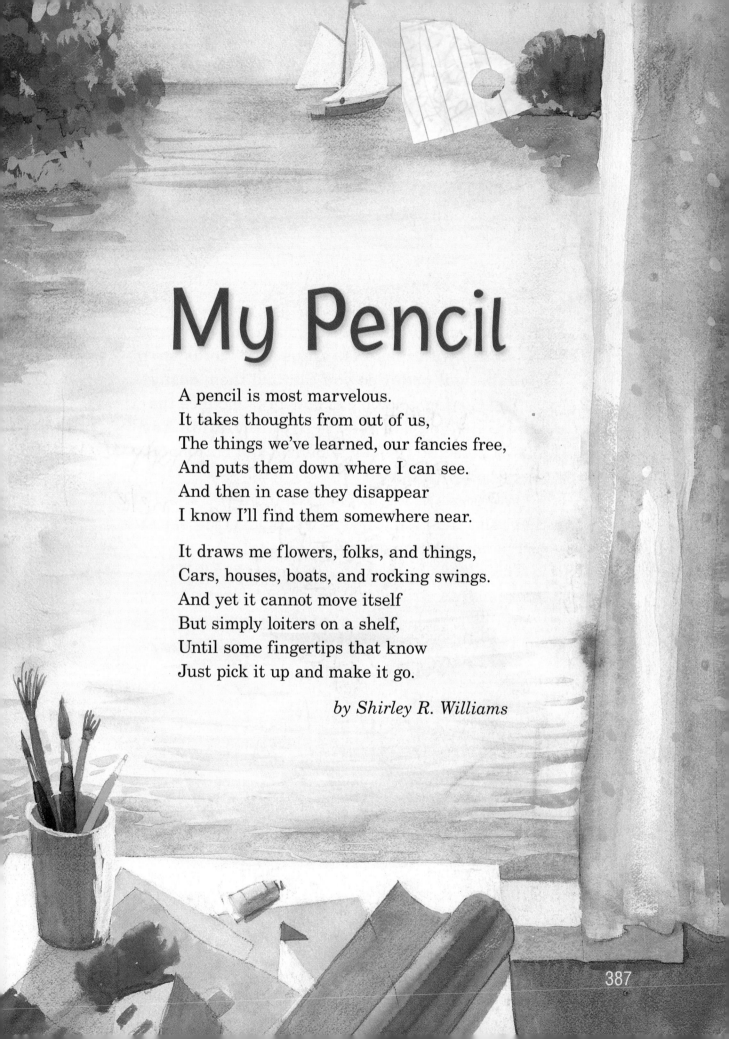

My Pencil

A pencil is most marvelous.
It takes thoughts from out of us,
The things we've learned, our fancies free,
And puts them down where I can see.
And then in case they disappear
I know I'll find them somewhere near.

It draws me flowers, folks, and things,
Cars, houses, boats, and rocking swings.
And yet it cannot move itself
But simply loiters on a shelf,
Until some fingertips that know
Just pick it up and make it go.

by Shirley R. Williams

Glossary

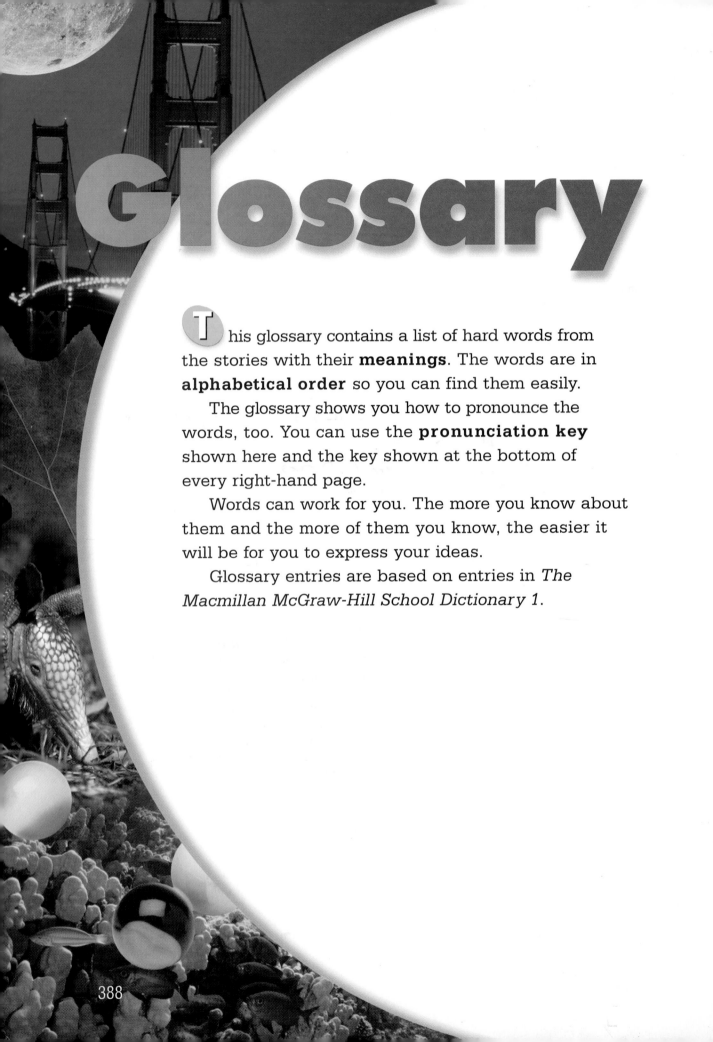

This glossary contains a list of hard words from the stories with their **meanings**. The words are in **alphabetical order** so you can find them easily.

The glossary shows you how to pronounce the words, too. You can use the **pronunciation key** shown here and the key shown at the bottom of every right-hand page.

Words can work for you. The more you know about them and the more of them you know, the easier it will be for you to express your ideas.

Glossary entries are based on entries in *The Macmillan McGraw-Hill School Dictionary 1*.

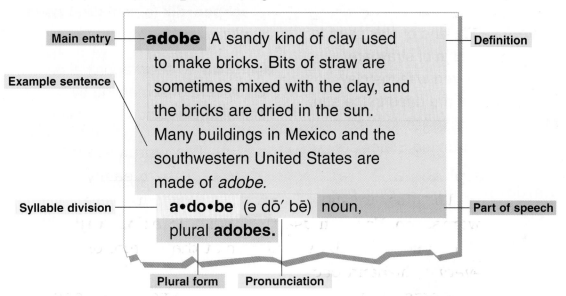

adobe/banner

First word on the page   Last word on the page

Sample Entry

Main entry — **adobe** A sandy kind of clay used to make bricks. Bits of straw are sometimes mixed with the clay, and the bricks are dried in the sun. Many buildings in Mexico and the southwestern United States are made of *adobe*. — Definition

Example sentence

Syllable division — **a•do•be** (ə dō′ bē) noun, plural **adobes.** — Part of speech

Plural form   Pronunciation

a	at, bad	d	dear, soda, bad
ā	ape, pain, day, break	f	five, defend, leaf, off, cough, elephant.
ä	father, car, heart		
âr	care, pair, bear, their, where	g	game, ago, fog, egg
e	end, pet, said, heaven, friend	h	hat, ahead
ē	equal, me, feet, team, piece, key	hw	white, whether, which
i	it, big, English, hymn	j	joke, enjoy, gem, page, edge
ī	ice, fine, lie, my	k	kite, bakery, seek, tack, cat
îr	ear, deer, here, pierce	l	lid, sailor, feel, ball, allow
o	odd, hot, watch	m	man, family, dream
ō	old, oat, toe, low	n	not, final, pan, knife
ô	coffee, all, taught, law, fought	ng	long, singer, pink
ôr	order, fork, horse, story, pour	p	pail, repair, soap, happy
oi	oil, toy	r	ride, parent, wear, more, marry
ou	out, now	s	sit, aside, pets, cent, pass
u	up, mud, love, double	sh	shoe, washer, fish, mission, nation
ū	use, mule, cue, feud, few	t	tag, pretend, fat, button, dressed
ü	rule, true, food	th	thin, panther, both,
u̇	put, wood, should	<u>th</u>	this, mother, smooth
ûr	burn, hurry, term, bird, word, courage	v	very, favor, wave
		w	wet, weather, reward
ə	about, taken, pencil, lemon, circus	y	yes, onion
b	bat, above, job	z	zoo, lazy, jazz, rose, dogs, houses
ch	chin, such, match	zh	vision, treasure, seizure

adobe A sandy kind of clay used to make bricks. Bits of straw are sometimes mixed with the clay, and the bricks are dried in the sun. Many buildings in Mexico and the southwestern United States are made of *adobe.*
  a•do•be (ə dō′ bē) *noun, plural* **adobes.**

Word History
The word **adobe** comes from the Spanish word of the same spelling, meaning "sun-dried brick." But the Spanish got this word from an even earlier Arabic word, *at-tob,* meaning "the brick."

anxious 1. Wanting very much; eager. I was *anxious* to make friends at my new school.
2. Nervous, worried or fearful about what may happen. My cousin was *anxious* about driving on the slippery roads.
  anx•ious (angk′ shəs *or* ang′ shəs) *adjective.*

appendix A short, hollow pouch that is attached to the large intestine.
  ap•pen•dix (ə pen′ diks) *noun, plural* **appendixes.**

applaud To show approval or enjoyment of something by clapping the hands. The children *applauded* the clown's funny tricks.
  ap•plaud (ə plôd′) *verb,* **applauded, applauding.**

arachnid Any of a large group of small animals without a backbone. The body of an arachnid is divided into two parts. Arachnids have four pairs of legs and no antennae or wings. Spiders, scorpions, mites, and ticks are *arachnids.*
  ar•ach•nid (ə rak′ nid) *noun, plural* **arachnids.**

area A particular space, region, or section. We moved from the city to a rural *area.*
  ar•e•a (âr′ ē ə) *noun, plural* **areas.**

astonish To surprise very much; amaze. The news that I had won the contest *astonished* me.
▲**Synonym:** astound
  as•ton•ish (ə ston′ ish) *verb,* **astonished, astonishing.**

Language Note
A **synonym** is a word that can be used for another word. A synonym for *astonish* is *surprise.*

attic The space just below the roof of a house. We use our *attic* to store trunks of old clothes.
    at•tic (at′ ik) *noun, plural* **attics.**

autograph To write one's name in one's own handwriting. Will you *autograph* a copy of your book for me? *Verb.* —A person's signature written in that person's own handwriting. *Noun.*
    au•to•graph (ô′ tə graf′) *verb,* **autographed, autographing;** *noun, plural* **autographs.**

Word History

The word **autograph** comes from the Greek words *autos,* meaning "self," and *graphein,* meaning "to write."

---

banner A flag or other piece of cloth that has a design and sometimes writing on it. The fans at the baseball game held up a *banner.*
    ban•ner (ban′ ər) *noun, plural* **banners.**

beauty A quality that makes a person or a thing pleasing to look at, hear, or think about. The garden is a place of *beauty.*
    beau•ty (bū′ tē) *noun, plural* **beauties.**

bewilder To confuse or puzzle; mix up. The student was *bewildered* by the math problem.
    be•wil•der (bi wil′ dər) *verb,* **bewildered, bewildering.**

black widow A black spider. The female black widow is poisonous and has a red mark on her body. The female black widow is larger than the male.
    black wi•dow (blak wid′ ō) *noun, plural* **black widows.**

blossom The flower of a plant or tree, especially one that produces fruit. We gathered *blossoms* from the apple trees. *Noun.*—To have flowers or blossoms; bloom. The peach trees *blossom* in the spring. *Verb.*
    blos•som (blos′ əm) *noun, plural* **blossoms;** *verb,* **blossomed, blossoming.**

---

at; āpe; fär; câre; end; mē; it; īce; pîerce; hot; ōld; sông; fôrk; oil; out; up; ūse; rüle; pull; tûrn; chin; sing; shop; thin; this; hw in white; zh in treasure. The symbol ə stands for the unstressed vowel sound in about, taken, pencil, lemon, and circus.

bronco busting The act of taming and training wild horses. The cowboys spent part of each day *bronco busting.*
    bron•co bust•ing (brong′ kō bust′ ing) *noun.*

buffalo 1. A large North American animal that has a big shaggy head with short horns and a hump on its back; bison. **2.** Any of various oxen of Europe, Asia, and Africa.
    buf•fa•lo (buf′ ə lō′) *noun, plural* **buffaloes** *or* **buffalos** *or* **buffalo.**

canyon A deep valley with very high, steep sides. A *canyon* often has a stream running through it.
    can•yon (kan′ yən) *noun, plural* **canyons.**

capture To catch and hold a person, animal, or thing. The explorers *captured* the tiger in a large net. ▲**Synonyms:** take, seize
    cap•ture (kap′ chər) *verb* **captured, capturing.**

ceiling The inside overhead surface of a room. The tall guest reached up and almost touched the *ceiling.*
    ceil•ing (sē′ ling) *noun, plural* **ceilings.**

celebrate To observe or honor a special day or event with ceremonies and other activities. We *celebrated* Grandma's birthday with a big party.
    cel•e•brate (sel′ ə brāt′) *verb,* **celebrated, celebrating.**

cent A coin of the United States and Canada. One hundred *cents* is equal to one dollar. ▲Other words that sound like this are **scent** and **sent.**
    ▲**Synonym:** penny
    cent (sent) *noun, plural,* **cents.**

Language Note

A **homonym** is a word that sounds like another word but has a different meaning. A homonym for *cent* is *sent.*

---

combine To cause to mix together; blend. We *combined* eggs, flour, and milk to make the batter for the pancakes.
    ▲**Synonyms:** blend, mix
    com•bine (kəm bīn′) *verb,* **combined, combining.**

concert A performance, usually a musical performance by a number of musicians. We went to a *concert* in the park.
▲**Synonyms:** show, recital, symphony
con•cert (kon′ sərt) *noun, plural* **concerts.**

conductor 1. A person who leads a group of musicians. Our music teacher is also the *conductor* of the school orchestra. **2.** A person on a train or bus who collects fares and assists passengers. The *conductor* walked down the aisle and called out the name of the next stop.
con•duc•tor (kən duk′ tər) *noun, plural* **conductors.**

consonant A letter of the alphabet that is not a vowel. *Consonants* include the letters *b, d, f, g, m, p, t,* and others.
con•so•nant (kon′ sə nənt) *noun, plural* **consonants.**

continue 1. To go on or do after stopping. We will *continue* the meeting after lunch. **2.** To keep on happening, being, or doing; go on without stopping. The rain had *continued* for two days.
con•tin•ue (kən tin′ ū) *verb,* **continued, continuing.**

cork The light, thick outer bark of a kind of oak tree. *Cork* is used for such things as bottle stoppers, insulation, and floats for rafts.
cork (kôrk) *noun, plural* **corks.**

correct Not having any mistakes; accurate. This is the *correct* answer to the arithmetic problem. *Adjective.*
—To mark the mistakes in; change to make right. The teacher *corrected* our spelling tests. *Verb.*
cor•rect (kə rekt′) *adjective; verb,* **corrected, correcting.**

costume Clothes worn in order to look like someone or something else. I wore a cowboy *costume* to the Halloween party.
cos•tume (kos′ tüm *or* kos′ tūm) *noun, plural* **costumes.**

at; āpe; fär; câre; end; mē; it; īce; pîerce; hot; ōld; sông; fôrk; oil; out; up; ūse; rüle; pull; tûrn; chin; sing; shop; thin; this; hw in white; zh in treasure. The symbol ə stands for the unstressed vowel sound in about, taken, pencil, lemon, and circus.

creep To move slowly along the ground or over a surface. The wind *creeps* in through the window.
　creep (krēp) *verb,* **crept, creeping.**

crooked Not straight; bent or curving. The path through the woods was very *crooked.*
　▲**Synonyms:** bent, winding
　crook•ed (krůk′ id) *adjective.*

crop Plants that are grown to be used as a food or to be sold for profit. Wheat and corn are two *crops* grown in the Midwest.
　crop (krop) *noun, plural* **crops.**

crumble 1. To break into small pieces. The muffin *crumbled* when I tried to butter it. **2.** To fall apart or be destroyed. The old house is slowly *cumbling.*
　crum•ble (krum′ bəl) *verb,* **crumbled, crumbling.**

daddy-longlegs A kind of bug that looks like a spider. A daddy-longlegs has a small, round body and eight very long, thin legs.
　dad•dy long•legs (dad′ē lông′ legz′) *noun, plural* **daddy-longlegs.**

darkness A partial or total absence of light; the result of a light going out. The sun dipped behind the hilltops and *darkness* fell.
　dark•ness (därk′ nis) *noun.*

dawn The first light that appears in the morning. We left our house before *dawn.*
　▲**Synonym:** daybreak
　dawn (dôn) *noun, plural* **dawns.**

deaf Not able to hear, or not able to hear well. The *deaf* children were using sign language to speak to one another
　deaf (def) *adjective,* **deafer, deafest.**

decimal 1. A period put before a decimal fraction. The periods in .5, .30, and .052 are *decimals.* **2.** A fraction with a denominator of 10, or a multiple of 10 such as 100 or 1,000. The *decimal* .5 is another way of writing $\frac{5}{10}$.
　dec•i•mal (des′ ə mel) *noun, plural* **decimals.**

den A place where wild animals rest or sleep. The bear uses a cave as a *den* during its long winter sleep.
den (den) *noun, plural* **dens.**

disaster An event that causes much suffering or loss. The flood was a *disaster.*
▲Synonyms: tragedy, trouble
dis•as•ter (di zas′ tər) *noun, plural* **disasters.**

Word History

The word **disaster** comes from the Latin *dis,* meaning "away," and *astrum,* meaning "star."

---

dragonfly An insect that has a long, thin body and two pairs of wings. *Dragonflies* eat mosquitoes and live near fresh water.
drag•on•fly (drag′ ən flī′) *noun, plural* **dragonflies.**

eager Wanting very much to do something. A person who is *eager* is full of interest and enthusiasm.
▲Synonym: excited
ea•ger (ē′ gər) *adjective.*

earthquake A shaking or trembling of the ground. Earthquakes are caused by rock, lava, or hot gases moving deep inside the earth. Some *earthquakes* are so powerful that they cause the ground to split.
earth•quake (ûrth′ kwāk′) *noun, plural* **earthquakes.**

echo The repeating of a sound. Echoes are caused when sound waves bounce off a surface. We shouted "hello" and soon heard the *echo* of our voices.
ech•o (ek′ ō) *noun, plural* **echoes.**

embarrass To make someone feel shy, uncomfortable, or ashamed. My foolish mistake *embarrassed* me.
em•bar•rass (em bar′ əs) *verb,* **embarrassed, embarrassing.**

enormous Much greater than the usual size or amount; very large. The flood caused an *enormous* amount of damage.
▲Synonyms: large, gigantic
e•nor•mous (i nôr′ məs) *adjective.*

---

at; āpe; fär; câre; end; mē; it; īce; pîerce; hot; ōld; sông; fôrk; oil; out; up; ūse; rüle; pull; tûrn; chin; sing; shop; thin; this; hw in white; zh in treasure. The symbol ə stands for the unstressed vowel sound in about, taken, pencil, lemon, and circus.

---

eon A very long period of time. That deposit of coal was formed *eons* ago.

　e•on (ē′ ən *or* ē′ on) *noun, plural* **eons.**

Espino, Fernando
　(es pē′ nō, fûr nän′ dō)

examine 1. To look at closely and carefully; check. We *examined* the baseball bat to be sure it wasn't cracked. **2.** To question in a careful way or test, usually to discover what a person knows. The lawyer *examined* the witness during the trial.

　▲**Synonyms:** inspect, study
　ex•am•ine (eg zam′ in) *verb,* **examined, examining.**

excitement The condition of being excited. We could hardly sleep because of our *excitement* about starting the trip tomorrow.

　ex•cite•ment (ek sīt′ mənt) *noun.*

fade 1. To lose freshness; wither. The flowers *faded* after three days. **2.** To lose or cause to lose color or brightness. Blue jeans may *fade* when they are washed.

　fade (fād) *verb,* **faded, fading.**

fan A person who is very interested in or enthusiastic about something. The *fans* ran up to the movie star.

　▲**Synonym:** admirer
　fan (fan) *noun, plural* **fans.**

feelers A part of an animal's body that is used for touching things. Many insects have *feelers* on their heads.

　feel•er (fē′ lər) *noun, plural* **feelers.**

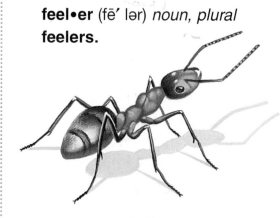

flex To bend. If your arm is tired, *flex* it to keep it loose.

　flex (fleks) *verb,* **flexed, flexing.**

flow To move along steadily in a stream. Water *flows* through these pipes.

　flow (flō) *verb,* **flowed, flowing.**

furniture Tables, chairs, beds, and other movable articles used in a home or office. Our living room is full of *furniture.*

　fur•ni•ture (fûr′ ni chər) *noun.*

gaze To look at something a long time. We all *gazed* at the beautiful sunset. *Verb.*—A long steady look. Our *gaze* rested on the bear and its two playful cubs. *Noun.*
> **gaze** (gāz) *verb,* **gazed, gazing;** *noun, plural* **gazes.**

Genghis Khan
> (geng′ gis kän′)

gift **1.** Something given; a present. This basketball was a *gift* from my parents. **2.** Talent; ability. That student has a *gift* for dancing.
> **gift** (gift) *noun, plural* **gifts.**

grain **1.** A tiny, hard piece of something. *Grains* of sand fell from the beach towel. **2.** The seed of wheat, corn, rice, oats, and other cereal plants. Breakfast cereal is made from *grains.*
> **grain** (grān) *noun, plural* **grains.**

groan To make a deep, sad sound. I *groaned* when the doctors touched my injured ankle.
> ▲**Synonym:** moan ▲ Another word that sounds like this is **grown.**
> **groan** (grōn) *verb,* **groaned, groaning.**

guard A person who is assigned to watch over things. The museum *guard* collected our tickets at the door. *Noun.*—To keep safe from harm or danger; protect. The dog *guarded* the house. *Verb.*
> **guard** (gärd) *noun, plural* **guards;** *verb,* **guarded, guarding.**

halfway To or at half the distance; midway. We climbed *halfway* up the mountain.
> **half•way** (haf′ wā) *adverb.*

handful **1.** The amount the hand can hold at one time. Each child took a *handful* of peanuts. **2.** A small number. Only a *handful* of people showed up.
> **hand•ful** (hand′ fūl′) *noun, plural* **handfuls.**

at; āpe; fär; câre; end; mē; it; īce; pîerce; hot; ōld; sông; fôrk; oil; out; up; ūse; rüle; pùll; tûrn; chin; sing; shop; thin; this; hw in white; zh in treasure. The symbol ə stands for the unstressed vowel sound in about, taken, pencil, lemon, and circus.

hatch To come from an egg. We are waiting for these chicks to *hatch.*

> **hatch** (hach) *verb,* **hatched, hatching.**

haunch A part of the body of a person or animal including the hip and upper thigh. The lion sat on its *haunches.*

> **haunch** (hônch) *noun, plural* **haunches.**

heap A collection of things piled together. We left a *heap* of peanut shells on the kitchen table.

> ▲ **Synonyms:** pile, load, mound
> **heap** (hēp) *noun, plural* **heaps.**

herd A group of animals that live or travel together. A *herd* of cattle grazed in the pasture.

> ▲ Another word that sounds like this is **heard.**
> **herd** (hûrd) *noun, plural* **herds;** *verb,* **herded, herding.**

ill Not healthy or well; sick. Many children in our class were *ill.*

> **ill** (il) *adjective.*

imaginary Existing only in the mind; unreal. Most people believe that elves are *imaginary.*

> ▲ **Synonyms:** unreal, fictional
> **i•mag•i•nary** (i maj′ə ner′ē) *adjective.*

include To have as part of the whole; contain. You don't have to buy batteries for that toy because they are already *included* in the box.

> **in•clude** (in klüd′) *verb,* **included, including.**

instrument **1.** A device for producing musical sounds. Our music teacher plays the guitar, flute, and several other *instruments.* **2.** A device used for doing a certain kind of work; tool. The dental hygienist used a sharp *instrument* to scrape my teeth.

> **in•stru•ment** (in′strə mənt) *noun, plural* **instruments.**

invent **1.** To make or think of for the first time; create. Do you know who *invented* the phonograph? **2.** To make up. I'm ashamed to say I *invented* an excuse for being late.

> **in•vent** (in vent′) *verb,* **invented, inventing.**

Word History

The word **invent** comes from a Latin word meaning "to come upon" or "find." The word *invent* was originally used to describe the finding of an answer, the solution to a problem, or the means to do something.

jagged Having sharp points that stick out. Some eagles build nests on *jagged* cliffs.

   jag•ged (jag′ id) *adjective.*

jingle To make or cause to make a tinkling or ringing sound. When the bell moved, it *jingled.*

   jingle (jing′gəl) *verb,* **jingled, jingling.**

journey A long trip. The Pilgrims crossed the Atlantic on their *journey* to the New World.

   jour•ney (jûr′ nē) *noun, plural* **journeys.**

kinship A relationship or close connection. There has always been a *kinship* between the two villages.

   kin•ship (kin′ ship′) *noun, plural* **kinships.**

lasso A long rope with a loop. A *lasso* is used to catch animals. *Noun.*
—To catch with a lasso. The cowhands will *lasso* the steer. *Verb.*

   las•so (la′sō *or* lasü′) *noun, plural* **lassos** *or* **lassoes;** *verb,* **lassoed, lassoing.**

lease To rent. The family *leased* a cabin for the summer. *Verb.*
—A written agreement for renting a house, apartment, or land. My parents signed a new *lease. Noun.*

   lease (lēs) *verb,* **leased, leasing;** *noun, plural* **leases.**

at; āpe; fär; câre; end; mē; it; īce; pîerce; hot; ōld; sông; fôrk; oil; out; up; ūse; rüle; půll; tûrn; chin; sing; shop; thin; this; hw in white; zh in treasure. The symbol ə stands for the unstressed vowel sound in about, taken, pencil, lemon, and circus.

399

legend A story passed down through the years that many people believe, but that is not entirely true. There are many *legends* about the knights of the Middle Ages.
   leg•end (lej′ənd) *noun, plural* **legends.**

length The distance from one end to the other end. The *length* of a football field is 100 yards.
   ▲**Synonym:** measure
   length (lengkth *or* length) *noun, plural* **lengths.**

liquid A form of matter that is not a solid or a gas. A liquid can flow easily. It can take on the shape of any container into which it is poured. Milk is a *liquid*.
   liq•uid (lik′wid) *noun, plural* **liquids.**

Little League A baseball league for children under thirteen years of age. We play for the West Side *Little League* on Saturday.
   Lit•tle League (lit′ əl lēg) *noun.*

locate 1. To put or settle in a particular place. The baker *located* the bakery in the shopping mall. **2.** To find the place or position of. He could not *locate* his glasses.
   lo•cate (lō′kāt) *verb,* **located, locating.**

longhorn A breed of cattle with very long horns. *Longhorns* were once common in the southwestern United States.
   long•horn (lông′ hôrn) *noun, plural* **longhorns.**

Mm

marvel To feel wonder and astonishment. We *marveled* at the acrobat's skill.
   mar•vel (mär′vəl) *verb,* **marveled, marveling.**

McGwire, Mark
   (mə gwīr′, märk)

mischievous Playful but naughty. That *mischievous* child hid my slippers again.
   mis•chie•vous (mis′chə vəs) *adjective.*

miserable 1. Very unhappy; wretched. We all felt *miserable* about losing our dog. **2.** Causing discomfort or unhappiness. I had a *miserable* cold.
▲ **Synonyms:** sad, horrible, unpleasant
mis•er•a•ble (miz′ ər ə bəl) *adjective.*

mob To crowd around in excitement or anger. Shoppers *mobbed* the store during the big sale. *Verb.* —A large number of people; crowd. A *mob* is sometimes made up of people who are so angry or upset about something that they break the law and cause damage. *Noun.*
mob (mob) *verb,* **mobbed, mobbing;** *noun, plural* **mobs.**

mock Not real; imitation. In history class we had a *mock* battle with cardboard shields. *Adjective.*—To make fun of in a mean way. Instead of helping, they laughed and *mocked* me when I fell off my bike. *Verb.*
mock (mok) *adjective; verb,* **mocked, mocking.**

musician A person who is skilled in playing a musical instrument, composing music, or singing. My brother studied piano for years and became a talented *musician.*
mu•si•cian (mū zish′ ən) *noun, plural* **musicians.**

mustang A wild horse that lives on the American plains; bronco. We watched the *mustangs* go down to the river for a cool drink of water.
mus•tang (mus′tang) *noun, plural* **mustangs.**

Nn

New World North and South America; the Western Hemisphere.
New World (nü wûrld)

Nilsson, Kerstin
(Nil′sən, Kûr′stin)

northern lights Shining bands of light that can be seen in the night sky in the Northern Hemisphere. In the winter, you can see the *northern lights* in Alaska.
north•ern lights (nôr′thərn līts) *noun.*

at; āpe; fär; câre; end; mē; it; īce; pîerce; hot; ōld; sông; fôrk; oil; out; up; ūse; rüle; půll; tûrn; chin; sing; shop; thin; this; hw in white; zh in treasure. The symbol ə stands for the unstressed vowel sound in about, taken, pencil, lemon, and circus.

Oo

orchestra **1.** A group of musicians playing together on various instruments. **2.** The area just in front of a stage in which the orchestra plays.
▲**Synonyms:** symphony, band
or•ches•tra (ôr′ kə strə) *noun, plural* **orchestras.**

Word History

The word **orchestra** comes from a Greek word meaning "dance area." In the theater of ancient Greece, one section of the stage was called the *orchestra*. It was there that a chorus of performers danced and sang during a performance.

Pp

palace A very large, grand building where a king, queen, or other ruler usually lives. In London, we got to visit Buckingham *Palace.*
pal•ace (pal′ is) *noun, plural* **palaces.**

Panama A country in Central America.
Pan•a•ma (pan′ ə mä′) *noun.*

pattern The way in which colors, shapes, or lines are arranged or repeated in some order. The wallpaper was printed with a pretty flower *pattern.*
▲**Synonym:** design
pat•tern (pat′ ərn) *noun, plural* **patterns.**

peak **1.** A high mountain, or the pointed top of a high mountain. We could see the snowy *peaks* in the distance. **2.** A sharp or pointed end or top. If you stand on the *peak* of our roof, you can see the ocean.
▲**Synonyms:** mountain top, crest, summit
peak (pēk) *noun, plural* **peaks.**

pedestrian A person who travels on foot; walker. Sidewalks are for *pedestrians.*
ped•es•tri•an (pə des′trē ən) *noun, plural* **pedestrians.**

percussionist One who is skilled in playing percussion instruments, such as the drum, cymbal, xylophone, and piano. The *percussionist* in the orchestra played the bass drum and cymbals.

> **per•cus•sion•ist** (pər kush′ ən ist) *noun, plural* **percussionists.**

petition A formal request that is made to a person in authority. All the people on our street signed a *petition* asking the city to put a stop sign on the corner. *Noun.*—To make a formal request to. The students in our school *petitioned* the principal to keep the library open on weekends. *Verb.*

> **pe•ti•tion** (pə tish′ ən) *noun, plural* **petitions;** *verb,* **petitioned, petitioning.**

pitcher A baseball player who throws the ball to the batter. The *pitcher* stands near the middle of the diamond facing home place.

> **pitch•er** (pich′ ər) *noun, plural* **pitchers.**

pitcher

prairie Flat or rolling land covered with grass. A *prairie* has few trees.
> ▲Synonym: plains
> **prai•rie** (prâr′ ē) *noun, plural* **prairies.**

prey An animal that is hunted by another animal for food. Rabbits and birds are the *prey* of foxes.
> **prey** (prā) *noun, plural* **prey.**

prong One of the pointed ends of an antler or of a fork or other tool. My grandmother's forks have only three *prongs.*
> ▲Synonym: point
> **prong** (prông *or* prong) *noun, plural* **prongs.**

at; āpe; fär; câre; end; mē; it; īce; pîerce; hot; ōld; sông; fôrk; oil; out; up; ūse; rüle; pùll; tûrn; chin; sing; shop; thin; this; hw in white; zh in treasure. The symbol ə stands for the unstressed vowel sound in about, taken, pencil, lemon, and circus.

pure 1. Nothing but. We won that game with *pure* luck. **2.** Not mixed with anything else. This bracelet is made of *pure* silver.
▲ **Synonyms:** true, actual
pure (pyür) *adjective,* **purer, purest.**

Rr

respect High regard or consideration. We show *respect* for our teacher. *Noun.*—To have or show honor or consideration for. I *respect* your opinion. *Verb.*
▲ **Synonyms:** admiration, esteem
re•spect (ri spekt′) *noun; verb,* **respected, respecting.**

ripe Fully grown and ready to be eaten. The tomatoes in the garden are *ripe* now.
ripe (rīp) *adjective,* **riper, ripest.**

royal Of or pertaining to a king or queen or their family. The *royal* family lives in the palace.
roy•al (roi′ əl) *adjective.*

rubble Rough, broken pieces of stone, rock, or other solid material. The rescue workers searched through the *rubble* of the collapsed building.
rub•ble (rub′ əl) *noun.*

ruin Harm or damage greatly. The earthquake *ruined* the town. *Verb.* —Destruction, damage, or collapse. The storekeeper faced financial *ruin. Noun.*
▲ **Synonym:** destroy
ru•in (rü′ in) *verb,* **ruined, ruining;** *noun, plural* **ruins.**

Ss

Sabana Grande
(sə bän′ə grän′ dā)

scatter 1. To spread or throw about in various places. The wind *scattered* the leaves all over the yard. **2.** To separate or cause to separate and go in different directions. The loud thunder *scattered* the cattle.
▲ **Synonyms:** cast, fling, sprinkle
scat•ter (skat′ ər) *verb,* **scattered, scattering.**

scene 1. The place where something happens. The police arrived on the *scene* just as the thieves were escaping. **2.** A part of an act in a play or movie.
▲Another word that sounds like this is **seen.**
scene (sēn) *noun, plural* **scenes.**

schedule The time at which something is supposed to happen. The train was running behind *schedule* because of the weather.
sched•ule (skej′ ül) *noun, plural* **schedules.**

score The points or a record of the points made in a game or on a test. The final *score* of the game was 5 to 4. *Noun.*—To make a point or points in a game or test. She *scored* 10 points for her basketball team. *Verb.*
score (skôr) *noun, plural* **scores;** *verb,* **scored, scoring.**

season 1. Any special part of the year. There is almost no rain during the dry *season.* **2.** One of the four parts of the year: spring, summer, fall, or winter.
sea•son (sē′ zən) *noun, plural* **seasons.**

season

Word History

The word **season** comes from a French word that originally meant, "the season of spring," or "planting time."

---

section 1. A part of an area or group. We visited the old *section* of the city. **2.** A part taken from a whole; portion. Please cut the apple into four *sections.*
▲**Synonym:** quarter
sec•tion (sek′ shən) *noun, plural* **sections.**

serious 1. Dangerous. Sam risked *serious* injury when he drove so fast on that icy road. **2.** Not joking; sincere. Were you *serious* about taking piano lessons?
▲**Synonyms:** grave, critical
se•ri•ous (sîr′ ē əs) *adjective.*

at; āpe; fär; câre; end; mē; it; īce; pîerce; hot; ōld; sông; fôrk; oil; out; up; ūse; rüle; pull; tûrn; chin; sing; shop; thin; this; hw in white; zh in treasure. The symbol ə stands for the unstressed vowel sound in about, taken, pencil, lemon, and circus.

405

shallow Not deep. The water in the pond is *shallow.*
shallow (shal′ ō) *adjective,* **shallower, shallowest.**

shelter **1.** To find or take refuge. It is not safe to take *shelter* under a tree during an electrical storm. **2.** To give shelter to. The umbrella *sheltered* us from the rain. *Verb.* —Something that covers or protects. The hikers used a cave as *shelter* during the thunderstorm. *Noun.*
shel•ter (shel′ tər) *verb,* **sheltered, sheltering;** *noun, plural* **shelters.**

skill The power or ability to do something. Swimming is an important *skill* to know when you are out on a boat.
▲ **Synonym:** talent
skill (skil) *noun, plural* **skills.**

sloth A slow-moving animal that lives in the forests of South America. *Sloths* use their long arms and legs and their curved claws to hang upside down from trees.
sloth (slôth *or* slōth) *noun, plural* **sloths.**

snipping The act or sound of cutting with scissors in short, quick strokes. *Snipping* coupons from the newspaper is a way to save money on groceries.
snip•ping (snip′ ing) *noun.*

soldier A person who is a member of an army. The *soldiers* marched in a parade.
sol•dier (sōl′ jər) *noun, plural* **soldiers.**

Sosa, Sammy
(sō′ sə, sam′ mē)

souvenir Something that is kept because it reminds one of a person, place, or event. I kept my ticket as a *souvenir* of my first play.
▲ **Synonym:** keepsake, memento
sou•ve•nir (sü′ və nîr′ *or* sü′ və nîr′) *noun, plural* **souvenirs.**

steamship A large ship that is powered by steam.
steam•ship (stēm′ ship) *noun, plural* **steamships.**

stem The main part of a plant that supports the leaves and flowers. Water and food travel through the *stem* to all parts of the plant.
▲ Synonym: stalk
stem (stem) *noun, plural* **stems.**

straighten 1. To make or become straight. The picture on the wall slanted to the left, so I *straightened* it. **2.** To put into proper order. I asked you to *straighten* your room.
straight•en (strā′tən) *verb,* **straightened, straightening.**

struggle To make a great effort. The children *struggled* through the heavy snow.
strug•gle (strug′ əl) *verb,* **struggled, struggling.**

stumble To lose one's balance; trip. I *stumbled* over the rake.
stum•ble (stum′ bəl) *verb,* **stumbled, stumbling.**

surround To be on all sides of; form a circle around. A fence *surrounds* our yard.
▲ Synonym: enclose
sur•round (sə round′) *verb,* **surrounded, surrounding.**

Sweden A country in northern Europe.
Swe•den (swē′ dən) *noun.*

tall tale A made-up or exaggerated story; a tale too fantastic to believe.
tall tale (tôl tāl) *noun, plural* **tall tales.**

Tanksi
(tawnk′ shē)

tarantula A hairy spider that is found in warm areas. The *tarantula* has a painful bite.
ta•ran•tu•la (tə ran′ chə lə) *noun, plural* **tarantulas.**

Tiblo
(tē′ blō)

toucan A bird that has a heavy body, a very large beak, and colorful feathers. *Toucans* are found in Central America.
tou•can (tü′ kan) *noun, plural* **toucans.**

at; āpe; fär; câre; end; mē; it; īce; pîerce; hot; ōld; sông; fôrk; oil; out; up; ūse; rüle; pull; tûrn; chin; sing; shop; thin; this; hw in white; zh in treasure. The symbol ə stands for the unstressed vowel sound in about, taken, pencil, lemon, and circus.

towering Very tall; lofty. *Towering* palm trees lined the beach.
tow•er•ing (tou′ ər ing) *adjective*.

trade To give one thing in return for something else. I'll *trade* you two of my cards for one of yours.
▲**Synonyms:** exchange, swap
trade (trād) *verb*, **traded, trading.**

triangle 1. A musical instrument made of a metal bar bent in the shape of a triangle. A *triangle* sounds like a bell when it is hit. **2.** A figure or object with three sides and three angles.
tri•an•gle (trī′ang′əl) *noun, plural* **triangles.**

trim To cut away or remove parts to make something neat and orderly. Please *trim* the hedge evenly.
trim (trim) *verb*, **trimmed, trimming.**

Uu

unusual Not usual, common, or ordinary. It is very *unusual* for them not to want to go to a movie.
un•u•su•al (un ū′ zhü əl) *adjective*.

Vv

vibration Rapid movement back and forth or up and down. People many miles away could feel the *vibration* of the earthquake.
▲**Synonym:** shaking
vi•bra•tion (vī brā′ shən) *noun, plural* **vibrations.**

visitor A person who visits. I have to clean my room because we're having *visitors* this afternoon.
▲**Synonym:** guest
vis•i•tor (viz′ i tər) *noun, plural* **visitors.**

Ww

wilderness A natural place where no people live. In a *wilderness* there may be a dense forest and wild animals.
wil•der•ness (wil′ dər nis) *noun, plural* **wildernesses.**

within In or into the inner part or parts of. The troops camped *within* the walls of the fort.
with•in (wi<u>th</u> in′ *or* with in′) *preposition*.

Woutilainen, Johan
(woo ti lā′ nən, yō′ han)

woven Formed or made by lacing together thread, yarn, or strips of straw or other material. Gold thread had been *woven* into the blouse.
wo•ven (wō′ vən) *past particple of* **weave.**

wrap To cover by putting something around. Please help me *wrap* these presents.
wrap (rap) *verb,* **wrapped, wrapping.**

Zz

zinnia A garden plant that has rounded, brightly colored flowers.
zin•ni•a (zin′ ē ə) *noun, plural* **zinnias.**

at; āpe; fär; câre; end; mē; it; īce; pîerce; hot; ōld; sông; fôrk; oil; out; up; ūse; rüle; pùll; tûrn; chin; sing; shop; thin; this; hw in white; zh in treasure. The symbol ə stands for the unstressed vowel sound in about, taken, pencil, lemon, and circus.

ACKNOWLEDGMENTS

The publisher gratefully acknowledges permission to reprint the following copyrighted material:

"Abuelita's Lap" by Pat Mora from CONFETTI: POEMS FOR CHILDREN by Pat Mora. Text copyright © 1996 by Pat Mora. Reprinted by permission of Lee & Low Books Inc.

Entire text and art and cover of CITY GREEN by DyAnne DiSalvo-Ryan. Copyright © 1994 by DyAnne DiSalvo-Ryan. By permission of Morrow Junior Books, a division of William Morrow and Company, Inc.

"Closed, I am a mystery" by Myra Cohn Livingston from A PLACE TO DREAM. From My Head is Red and Other Riddle Rhymes by Myra Cohn Livingston. Copyright © 1990 by Myra Cohn Livingston (Published by Holliday House, NY) by presmission of Marian Reiner.

"Different Drum" by Joe Scruggs from ANTS by Joe Scuggs. (Produced by Gary Powell.) Copyright © 1994 by Educational Graphics Press, Inc.

"Dream Wolf" is from DREAM WOLF by Paul Goble. Copyright © 1990 by Paul Goble. Reprinted with the permission of Simon & Schuster Books For Young Readers.

"Fog" by Carl Sandburg from CHICAGO POEMS by Carl Sandburg. Copyright © 1916 by Holt Reinhart & Winston Inc.; renewed 1944 by Carl Sandburg. Reprinted by permission of Harcourt Brace Jovanovich, Inc.

Cover permission for THE GIRL WHO LOVED WILD HORSES by Paul Goble. Copyright © 1978 by Paul Goble. Reprinted by permission of Simon & Schuster Books for Young Readers.

"Grandfather's Journey" by Allen Say. Copyright © 1993 by Allen Say. Reprinted with the permission of Houghton Mifflin Company. All rights reserved.

"The Little Painter of Sabana Grande" by Patricia Maloney Markun, illustrated by Robert Casilla. Text copyright © 1993 by Patricia Maloney Markun. Illustrations copyright © 1993 by Robert Casilla. Published by Simon & Schuster Books for Young Readers. Reprinted by permission.

"Max Malone" from/"Baseballs for Sale" from MAX MALONE MAKES A MILLION by Charlotte Herman. Text copyright © 1991 by Charlotte Herman. Originally illustrated by Catherine Bowman Smith. Reprinted by permission of Henry Holt and Company, LLC.

"Moses Goes to a Concert" by Issac Millman. Copyright © 1998 by Isaac Millman. Reprinted by permission of Frances Foster Books/Farrar, Straus and Giroux.

"My Pencil" by Shirley R. Williams from POETRY PLACE ANTHOLOGY by Instructor Publications, Inc. Text copyright © 1983 by Instructor Publications, Inc.

"Opt: An Illusionary Tale" from OPT: AN ILLUSIONARY TALE by Arline and Joseph Baum. Copyright © 1987 by Arline and Joseph Baum. Used by permission of Viking Penguin, a division of Penguin Putnam, Inc.

"The Patchwork Quilt" from THE PATCHWORK QUILT by Valerie Flournoy, illustrations by Jerry Pinkney. Text copyright © 1985 by Valerie Flournoy. Illustrations copyright © 1985 by Jerry Pinkney. Published by arrangment Dial Books for Young Readers, a division of Penguin Putnam, Inc.

"Phoebe and the Spelling Bee" by Barney Saltzberg. Text and illustrations © 1996 by Barney Saltzberg. Reprinted by permission of Hyperion Books for Children.

Cover permission for RABBIT MAKES A MONKEY OUT OF LION by Verna Aardema; pictures by Jerry Pinkney. Pictures copyright © 1989 by Jerry Pinkney. Reprinted with the permission of Dial Books for Young Readers, a division of Penguin Books USA, Inc.

"The Sun, the Wind and the Rain" from THE SUN, THE WIND AND THE RAIN by Lisa Westberg Peters. Text copyright © 1988 by Lisa Westberg Peters. Illustrations copyright © 1988 by Ted Rand. Reprinted by permission of Henry Holt and Co., Inc.

Cover permission for TURTLE IN JULY by Marilyn Singer; illustrated by Jerry Pinckney. Illustrations copyright © 1989 by Jerry Pinckney. Reprinted with the permission of Atheneum Books for Young Readers, an imprint of Simon & Schuster.

"Who Am I?" by Felice Holman. Copyright © Felice Holman from AT THE TOP OF MY VOICE AND OTHER POEMS. Published by Charles Scribner's Sons, 1970.

"My Pencil" by Shirley R. Williams in POETRY PLACE ANTHOLOGY, published by Scholastic Professional Books. Copyright © 1983 by Edgell Communications, Inc. Reprinted with premission of Scholastic Inc.

Illustration

Myron Grossman, 105; B.B. Sams, 108–123; Pat Rasch, 107; Andy Levine, 171; Pat Rasch, 224; Vilma Ortiz–Dillon, 231, 234, 236; Mike DiGiorgio, 232, 237, 242; Andy Levine, 243; Mike DiGiorgio, 288; John Kanzler, 352–371; Leonor Glynn, 374; Tom Foty, 10–11 Marni Backer, 138–139 Greg Couch, 140–141 Christopher Zacharow, 254–255 Steve Barbaria, 256–257 Peter M. Fiore, 386–387; Rodica Prato, 391, 396, 407; George Thompson, 399.

Photography

12–13: The Bridgeman Art Library International/Christopher Wood Gallery, London UK. 48–49: Jane Wooster Scott/Superstock. 78–79: Art Resource, Inc./Herscovici. 50: t.l. Courtesy of Hyperion Press/Barry E. Levine. 106–107: The Norman Rockwell Museum at Stockbridge. 128–129: The Bridgeman Art Library International/Wingfield Sporting Gallery, London, UK. 135: Duomo/William Sallaz. 142–143: The Image Works/Cameramann. 172–173: The Bridgeman Art Library International/Bonhams, London, UK. 204–205: Art Resource, Inc./K.S. Art. 226–227: Madison Press Books. 228: m.l. Courtesy of Diane Hoyt–Goldsmith/Lawrence Migdale. 228–229: DRK Photo/(c) Tom Bean 1990. 230: DRK Photo/(c) Larry Ulrich. 231: Animals Animals/(c) Bill Beatty. 233: DRK Photo/(c) Stephen J. Kraseman. 236: Photo Researchers, Inc./(c) Scott Camazine. 238: ENP Images/(c) Gerry Ellis. 239: Photo Researchers, Inc./(c) Jewel Craig. 244–245: The Bridgeman Art Library International/Kathryn Kooyahoema/Jerry Jacka Photography. 250: b. Photo Researchers, Inc.. m. Photo Researchers, Inc. 258–259: Superstock/Gil Mayers. 260: t.r. reprinted by permission of Farrar, Straus and Giroux Books for Young Readers/(c) Daniel Lee. 318–319: Photo by William C.L. Weintraub for the Georgia Quilt Project, Inc. . 350–351: Gerald Peters Gallery, Santa Fe, New Mexico. . 376–377: Superstock. 383: Peter Arnold, Inc./(c) Kim Heacox.